Strength Training for Rugby League and Rugby Union

Strength Training for Rugby League and Rugby Union

Bruce Walsh

Kangaroo Press

More individuals are born than can possibly survive. The slightest advantage or better adaption in one being over those with which it comes into competition, in however slight a degree, will turn the balance.

Charles Robert Darwin, *On the Origin of Species*

Acknowledgments

Photographs courtesy Mirror Australian Telegraph Publications and U.S. Weightlifting Federation.

Cover photograph by *Rugby League Week.*

Reprinted 1991 and 1995
First published in 1990 by Kangaroo Press Pty Ltd
3 Whitehall Road NSW Kenthurst Australia 2156
P.O. Box 6125 Dural Delivery Centre NSW 2158
Typeset by G.T. Setters Pty Limited
Printed in Singapore through Global Com Pte Ltd

ISBN 0 86417 293 1

Contents

Lager.

Introduction

Rugby League and Rugby Union are all about skill, strength and power, speed and agility, endurance, and last but by no means least, commitment and courage. Of all the abovementioned factors, skill, commitment and courage are the major prerequisites for player performance at elite levels.

However, all things being equal, the stronger, faster, fitter team will emerge the winner. Individually, not only is a stronger player a better performer but, equally important, also physically more able to withstand the rigours of body contact football. Preparing the body for football is assuming ever increasing importance. In this modern era coaches are placing considerably greater emphasis on both attack and defence, with the result that physical stress to players is at an all time high.

While some form of strength training for football has been in vogue over the last two decades much confusion has existed as to how this is best implemented. To further compound this situation there has been a certain amount of mistrust regarding strength training on the part of some sections of the coaching fraternity. Many coaches and players are enthusiastic about strength training in the off season but hesitate about its value during the playing season. Others only believe in light resistance, while some support upper body training but are still dubious regarding the lower body counterpart, believing it to have a negative effect on speed.

The major problem facing players and coaches alike is the question of what constitutes the best form of strength training for football. Most strength training programs work to a lesser or greater degree. However there is a considerable amount of misinformation in existence, particularly in the areas of specificity and programming. There is a tendency for uniformity with little thought given to the varying needs of each individual player.

This text is aimed at eliminating this confusion and enabling both the player and coach to design a strength program catering for the diverse requirements of individuals, a program that will produce maximal results in the limited amount of time available to most players. Finally the reader will be better equipped to understand not only the practicalities of strength training for football, but also the rationale governing it.

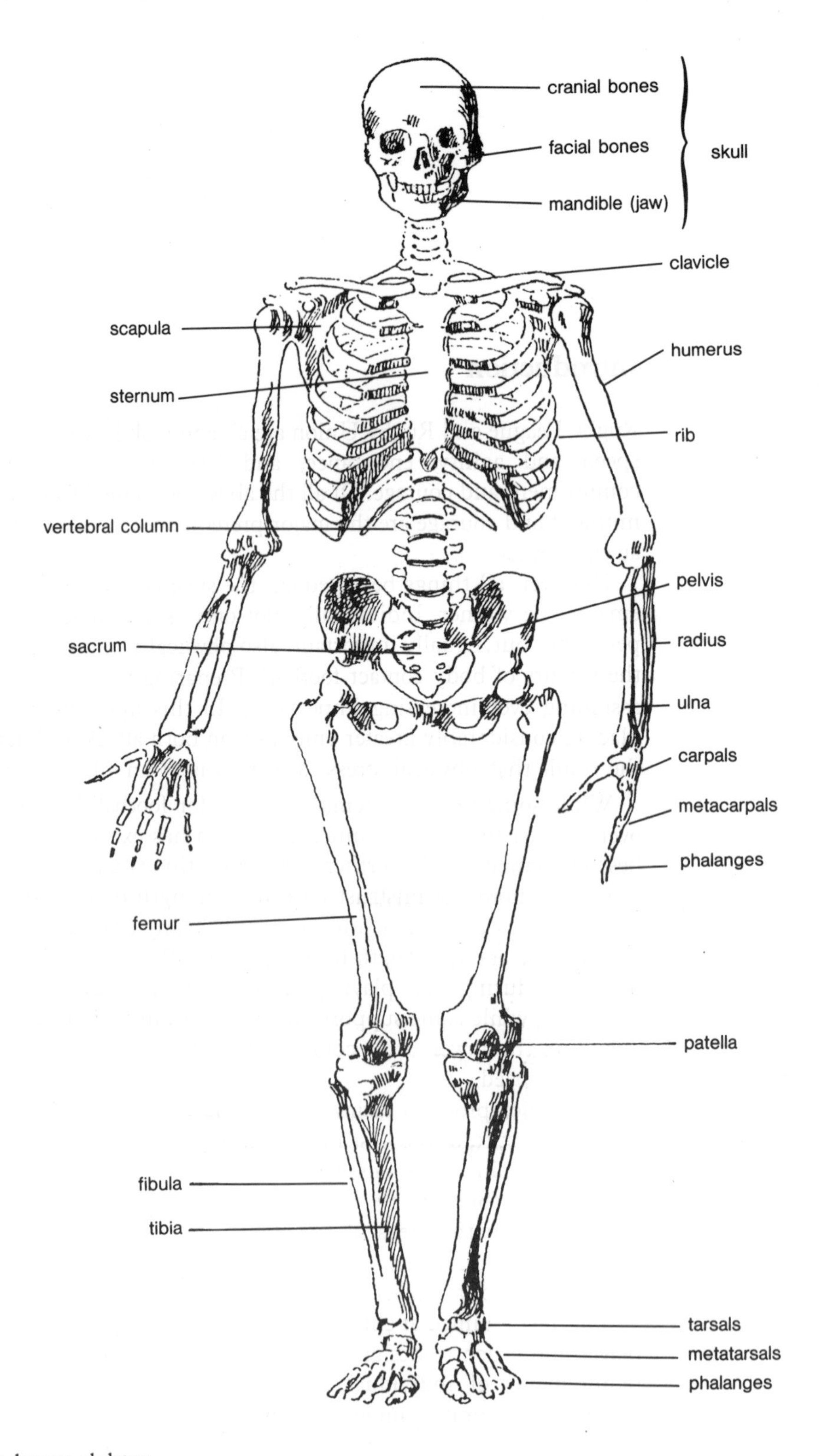

Fig. 1.1 The human skeleton

1. How the Body Moves

By failing to prepare you are preparing to fail.

The human skeletal system consists of some 226 bones, many of which are connected through a variety of joints. When muscles crossing these joints shorten or lengthen movement occurs. The study of this movement is called kinesiology. While it is beyond the scope of this text, and to a large degree the interest of the reader, to delve deeply into this subject, the writer believes that a basic knowledge of the major joints of the body and the muscles involved will enable the reader to have a better understanding of the principles and methodology of this publication. This particularly applies to the chapters on exercises and programs.

Some basic terminology of muscle and joint movement

Joints are the connection between two or more bones.

Joints are the connection between two or more bones. They can either be fixed (or of little movement) or have a large degree of mobility such as the knee, hip, arm, shoulder etc. It is these moveable joints, used mostly during excercise, which are of major relevance to the contents of this book. They operate in a number of directions (planes and axes) and are named in accordance with their axis of movement. These types of joints are illustrated in Fig. 1.4.

Some of the joints of the body come under several categories. For instance while the knee joint is commonly referred to as a hinge joint, it is a combination of hinge and pivot. The reason for this is that besides flexion and extension (straightening and bending), when bent the knee has a certain amount of inward and outward rotation. Much the same can be said about the elbow joint.

The shortening and lengthening of muscles across a joint causes movement.

Muscles There are over 400 skeletal muscles in the body of which some 75 are involved in joint action. The others are small and involved with minute actions such as voice production, facial expressions and swallowing.

It is the shortening and lengthening of some of these active muscles across a joint (or joints) that causes movement. When the angle of a joint

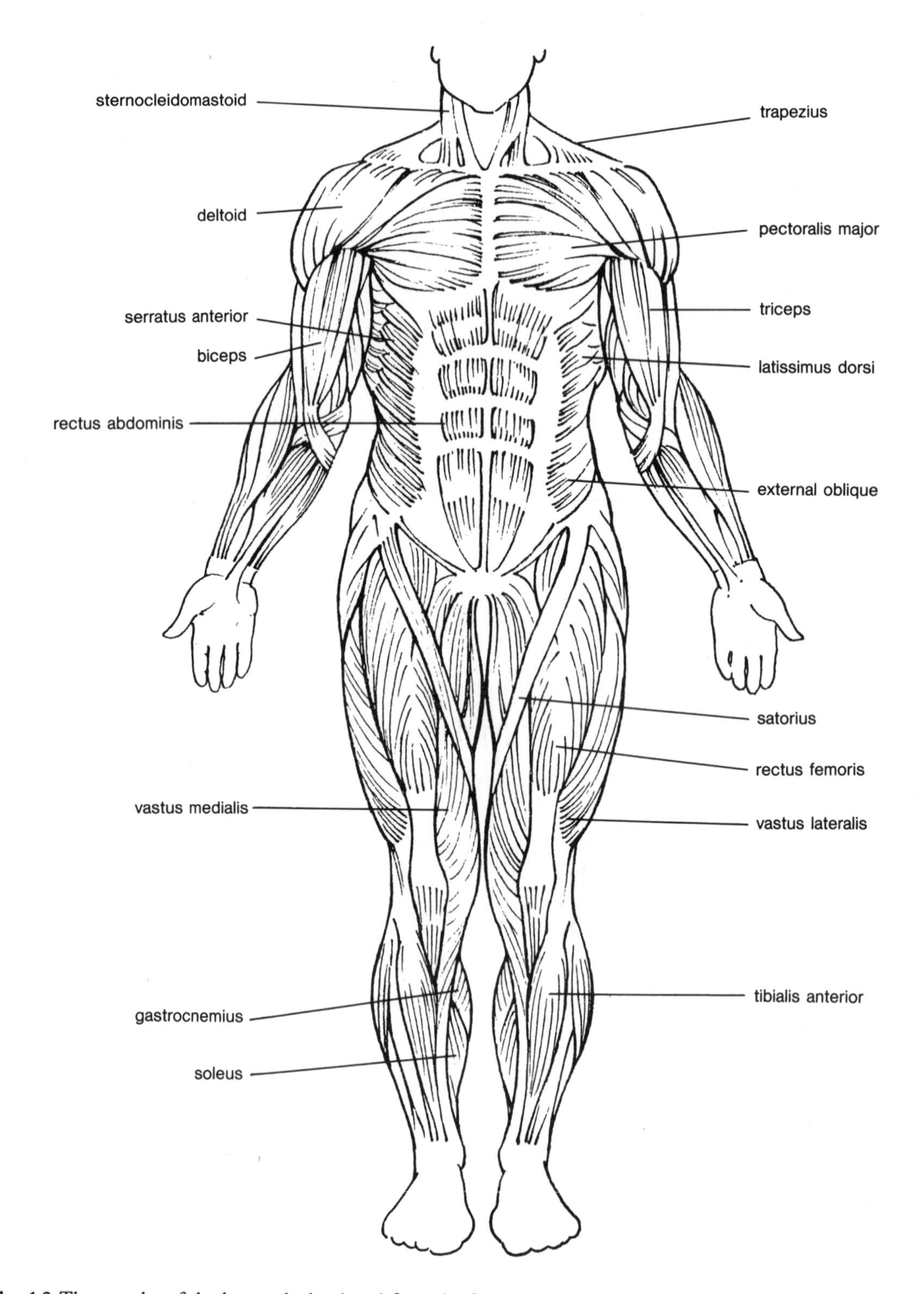

Fig. 1.2 The muscles of the human body viewed from the front

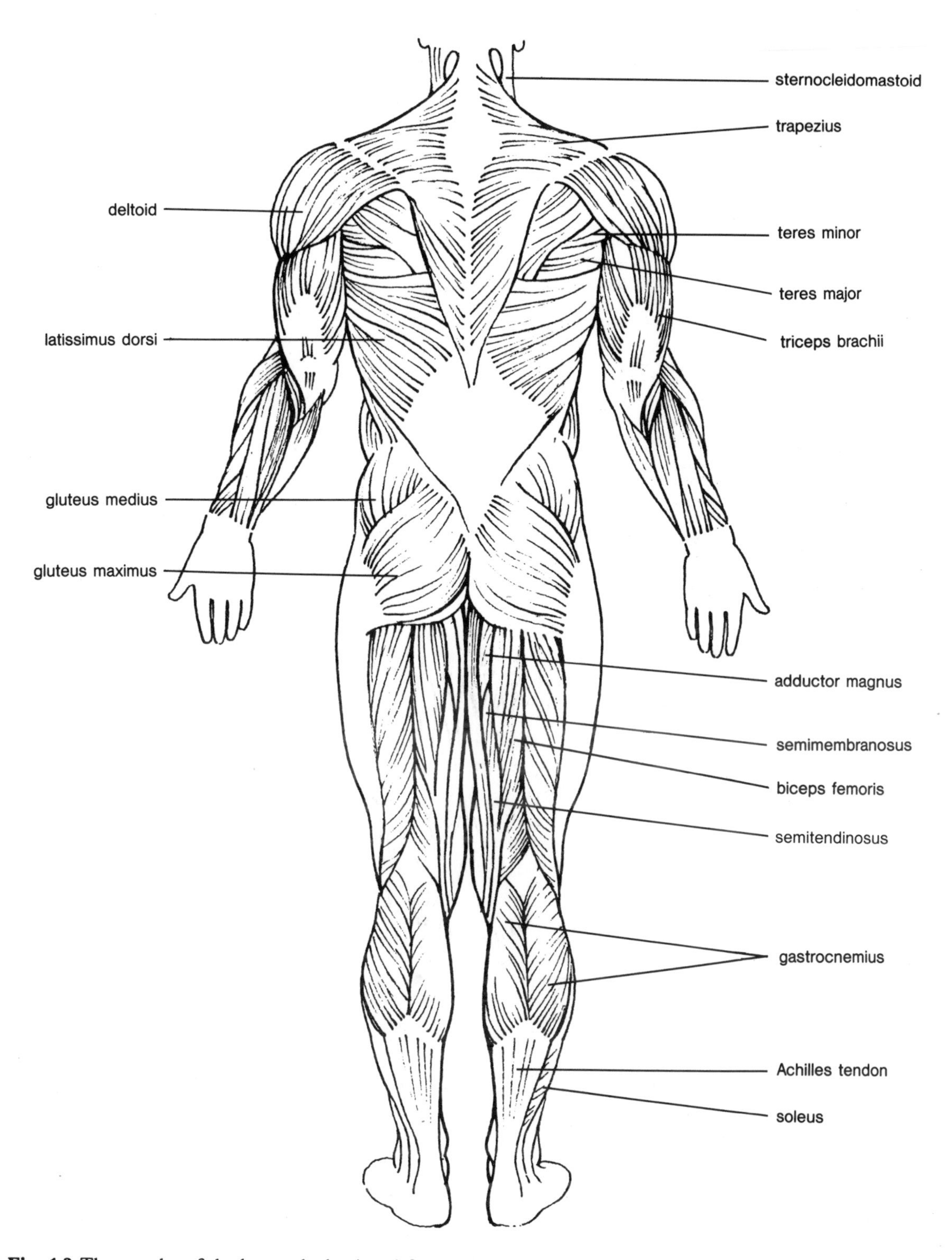

Fig. 1.3 The muscles of the human body viewed from the back

Ball and socket joint
(movement round three axes)

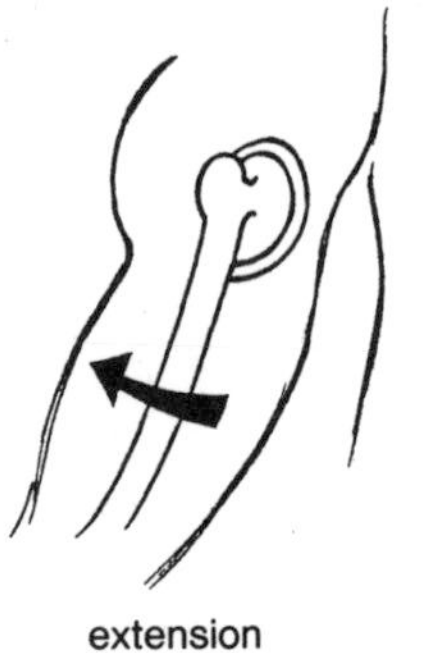

flexion

inward rotation

adduction

Condyloid joint
(movements round two axes)

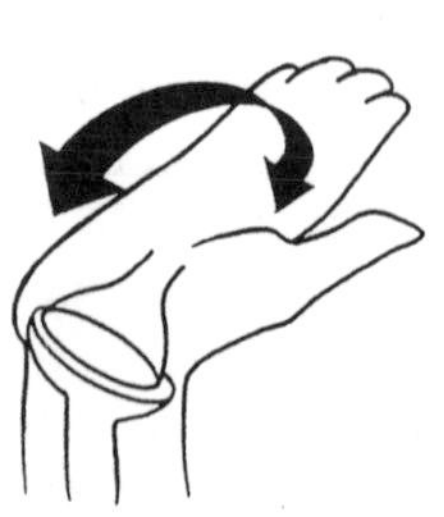

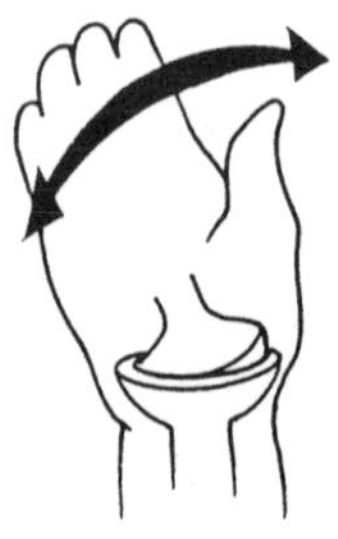

Pivot joint
(movement round one axis only)

inward rotation (pronation)

outward rotation (supination)

Gliding joint
(multiaxial)

small versatile movements

Hinge joint
(movement in one plane only)

stretching (extension)

bending (flexion)

Saddle joint
(movements round two axes)

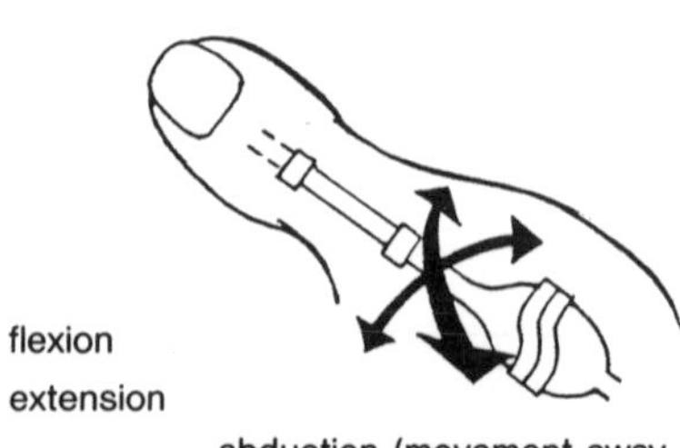

Fig. 1.4 Moveable joint types

narrows (flexion), such as in bending the arm or knee, one group of muscles shortens and simultaneously another group lengthens. The first group that shortens or contracts is known as agonists or flexors, while the second that lengthens is known as antagonists or extensors.

When the joint is straightened (extended) the angle of the joint becomes greater and the opposite procedure takes place, i.e. what was formerly the lengthened muscle (antagonist) now shortens and becomes the agonist with the previous agonist lengthening and assuming the role of antagonist. It is this agonist/antagonist pattern that gives the body co-ordinated movement. Fig. 1.5 illustrates agonist/antagonist movement of the elbow.

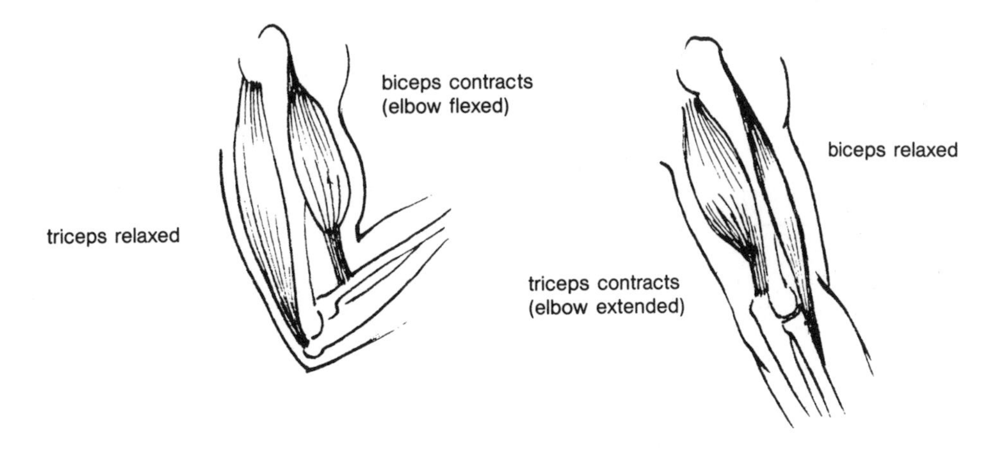

Fig. 1.5 The agonist/antagonist muscles of the elbow joint

The muscles that bear major responsibility for a movement are called prime movers.

Prime movers When a specific joint action takes place a number of muscles contribute to this action. The muscle(s) that bears the major responsibility is called the prime mover(s).

Assistant movers These are muscles that assist the prime mover in a specific joint action.

Stabilisers Sometimes called fixators, these muscles help stabilise (fix) a joint during a specific joint action. A good example of a stabiliser is the stomach (abdominal) muscles when a person is performing push ups. While the arms, shoulders, and chest muscles are the prime movers and assistant movers, the abdominals contract isometrically (without movement) and prevent the stomach from sagging and coming into contact with the floor, i.e. stabilising the hip joint so that the shoulder and elbow joint can move without interference. Indeed it is not uncommon for overweight, unfit people to have weak stomach muscles which prevent them from correctly performing push ups. Thus it can be seen stabilisers play an important role in exercise.

Neutralisers These are muscles which contract in order to counteract (rule out) an undesired action of another contracting muscle. They are sometimes referred to as synergists.

Tendons and ligaments Muscles are attached to bones by means of tendons and generally have attachments that span one or two joints. Ligaments help hold bones together at joints but, unlike muscles, cannot contract. While these ligaments give the joint stability, they are relatively inelastic and respond poorly to dislocation of the joint, generally caused by excessive force, a situation of some prevalence in football. Fig. 1.6 illustrates the iliofemoral and pubofemoral ligaments, both involved in stabilising the junction of the upper leg and hip. As a point of interest the iliofemoral is the strongest of all ligaments in the body and is capable of withstanding considerable stress.

Ligaments respond poorly to excessive force.

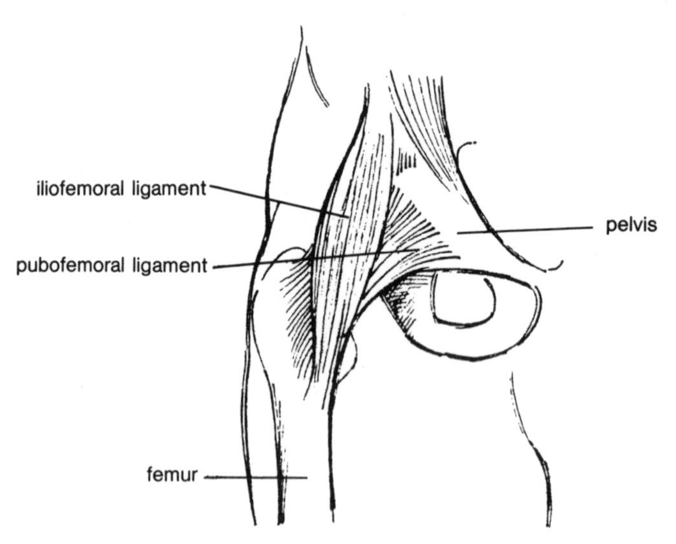

Fig. 1.6 The stabilising ligaments of the upper leg and hip

Joints

Let us now examine the major joints of the body and the prime movers involved in their movement. For their location refer to the anatomical illustrations at the commencement of this text.

The ankle joint

The major movements of the ankle joint in sporting activities are plantar flexion (lifting your heels off the ground) and dorsi flexion (raising the toes and ball of the foot). The action of plantar flexion takes place while both walking and running. The major muscle groups responsible for these actions are referred to as the calf muscles and consist of two muscles,

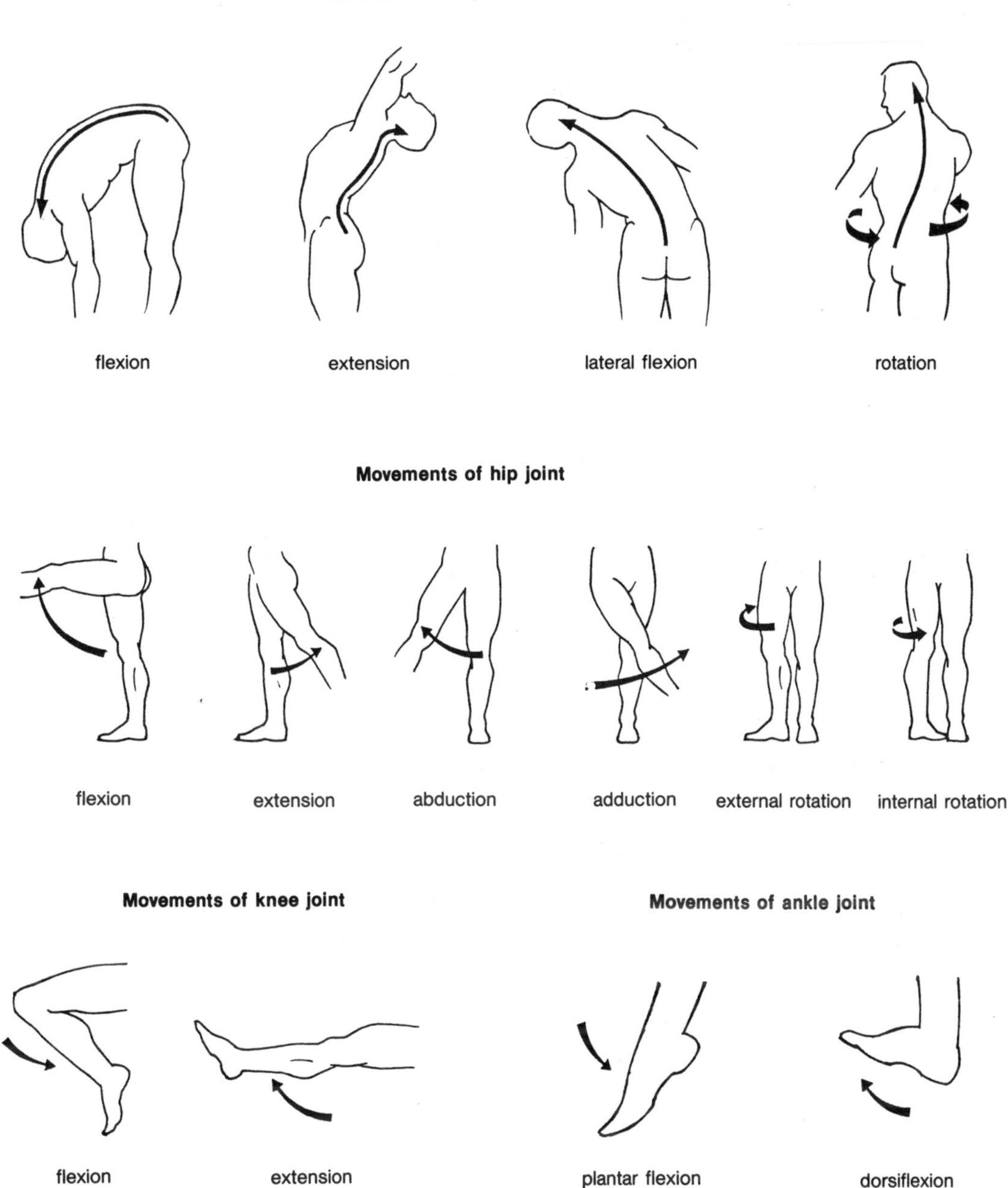

Fig. 1.7 The range of movements of various joints

the soleus (the walking muscle) and the gastrocnemius (sprinting muscle). In terms of dorsi flexion the major responsibility for this movement lies with a long narrow muscle located on the outside edge of the shin called the tibialis anterior. The gastrocnemius, because of its attachment across the knee joint, is also involved in knee flexion.

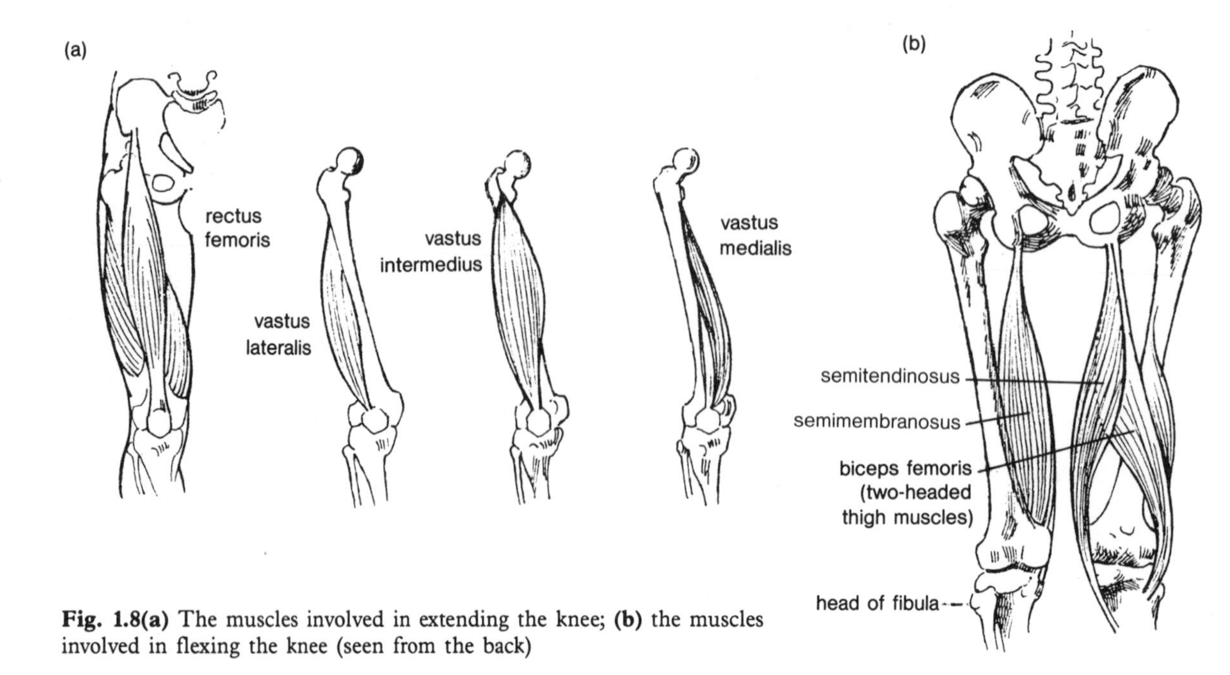

Fig. 1.8(a) The muscles involved in extending the knee; **(b)** the muscles involved in flexing the knee (seen from the back)

The knee joint

As previously mentioned the knee joint is primarily a hinge joint (although there is some lateral movement). It is a very important joint in football and must support the body weight in many complex agility movements as well as withstand considerable external force. The ligaments of this joint are the first line of defence. However the various muscle groups involved in knee action cross the front and back of the joint and also aid in stabilising it.

The muscles around the knee stabilise it.

The stabilising action of muscles around a joint applies to a greater or lesser extent to most joints of the body and is one of the reasons strength training aids in minimising injury in contact sports such as football. Another factor is that strength training also has a positive effect on connective tissue such as tendons and ligaments, etc.

Lack of strength causes injury.

The movement of straightening the knee (extension) is controlled by a group of four muscles collectively known as the quadriceps—rectus femoris, vastus lateralis, vastus medialis and vastus intermedius. The action of rising from a squatting position is very dependent on this group of muscles. They are illustrated in Figure 8.1(a).

Strong hamstring muscles are important in football.

The opposite action of extending the knee is to bend (flex) it. The muscles responsible for this action are located at the rear of the upper leg and are known as the hamstring group—biceps femoris, semitendinosus, semimembranosus. This group of muscles is heavily involved in sprinting and weakness in this area can be a major factor in hamstring 'pulls', a problem very familiar to football players and coaches. Figure 8.1(b) shows the muscles of the hamstring group.

The hip joint

This joint is of the ball and socket type and as such can move in all directions. This is clearly illustrated in Figs. 1.4 and 1.7. Flexion of the hip involves a number of muscle groups with the prime movers being the rectus femoris and the iliopsoas group.

While the rectus femoris is part of the quadricep muscle group (responsible for knee extension), it also crosses the hip joint and aids in hip flexion. In view of this dual action the rectus femoris is often referred to as the 'kicker's muscle', playing a major part in kicking a football.

The iliopsoas group (iliacus and psoas major) is a powerful hip flexor situated deep within the abdominal area. The psoas is attached to the lower spine and more will be said about this group of muscles when discussing abdominal exercises.

The hamstrings serve two functions—knee flexion and hip extension.

Hip extension prime movers are the hamstring group and the largest of the group of muscles that comprises the buttocks, the gluteus maximus. As previously mentioned the hamstrings are also responsible for knee flexion, and so are a 'two joint' muscle similar to the rectus femoris.

The other two 'glutes' (medius and minimus) control hip abduction—moving the leg away from the centre line. The reverse movement, hip adduction, has as its prime movers the adductor group (magnus, longeus and brevis).

See Figs. 1.9 and 1.10 for illustrations of hip joint muscles.

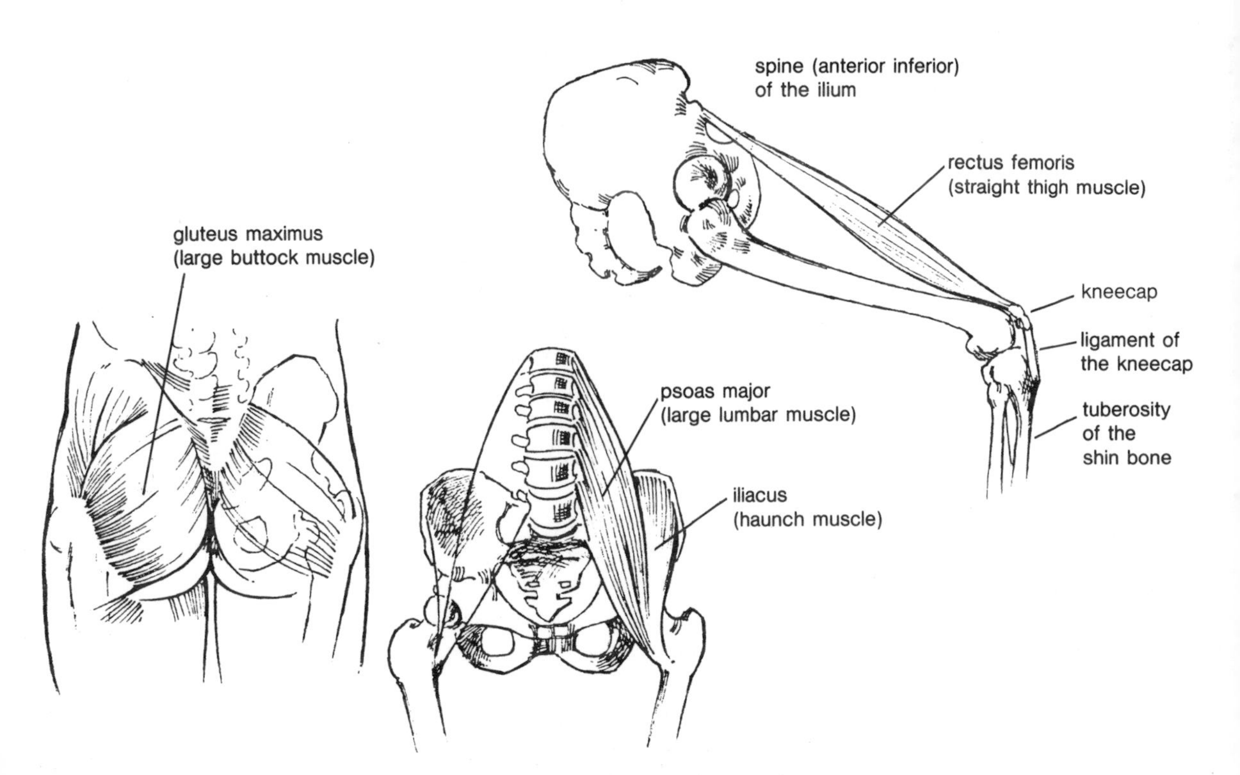

Fig. 1.9 Major muscles of the hip viewed from behind

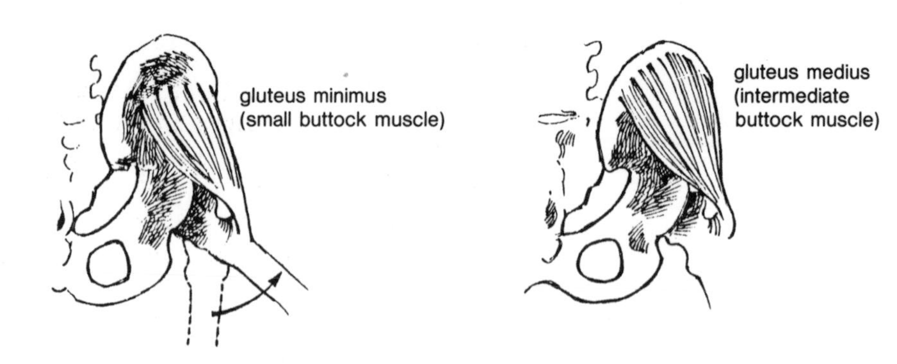

Fig. 1.10 Muscles controlling hip abduction

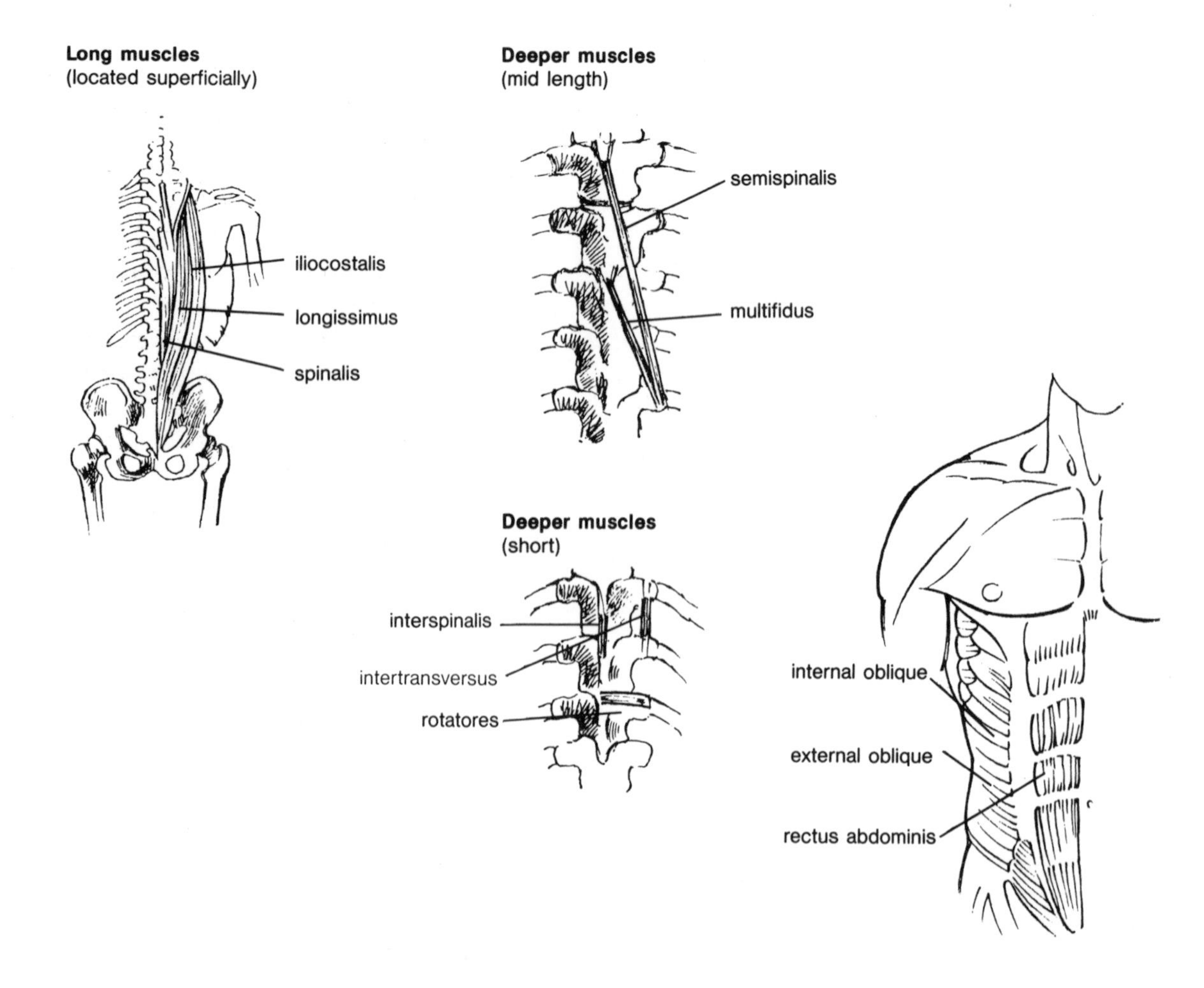

Fig. 1.11 Complex musculature of the spinal erectors, and the muscles of the abdominal group

The spinal column

Stomach and lower back muscles stabilise the spinal column.

If Fig. 1.7 is examined it will be seen that the spinal column moves in four directions—flexion, extension, lateral flexion and rotation. The most important muscle groups in these movements are the spinal erectors and the abdominal muscles.

The spinal erectors are a group of many muscles that extend from the buttocks on both sides of the spinal column and join various parts of the skeletal spinal vertebrae and posterior rib surface. They are generally classified into three groups—the long back muscles, back muscles of average length and short back muscles. All these groups are shown and named in Fig. 1.11. The muscles work together as a unit. The iliocostalis, however, is more adapted for taking part in sideward bending than the remaining muscles. The most important muscles for turning the trunk are the rotatores. The major responsibility of the spinal erectors is to extend, hyperextend and laterally flex the spine.

The abdominal group consists of the rectus abdominis and internal and external obliques. These are also illustrated in Fig. 1.11. The abdominals control spinal flexion, with the obliques important in both rotational and lateral flexion.

As a point of interest, in order to maintain correct posture and a level pelvis, the upward pull of the abdominals has the effect of balancing the downward pull of the hip flexors, while the upward pull of the spinal erectors operates in the same fashion in regard to the hip extensors. In view of the importance of the spinal erectors and abdominals in stabilising the spinal column it is essential that these muscles be thoroughly exercised.

Also, strong stomach muscles, when tensed during the performance of exercises involving the lower back, assist in relieving the stress on the vertebral discs. Many people have abdominals that are too weak in relation to their back muscles and require specific strengthening.

Neck strength in football should never be neglected.

Some of the spinal erector group (located at the upper extremity of the vertebrae) are responsible for lateral flexion, extension and rotation of the head. Other neck muscles of consequence are the sternocleidomastoid and scaleni, prime movers in flexion, and rotation of the head

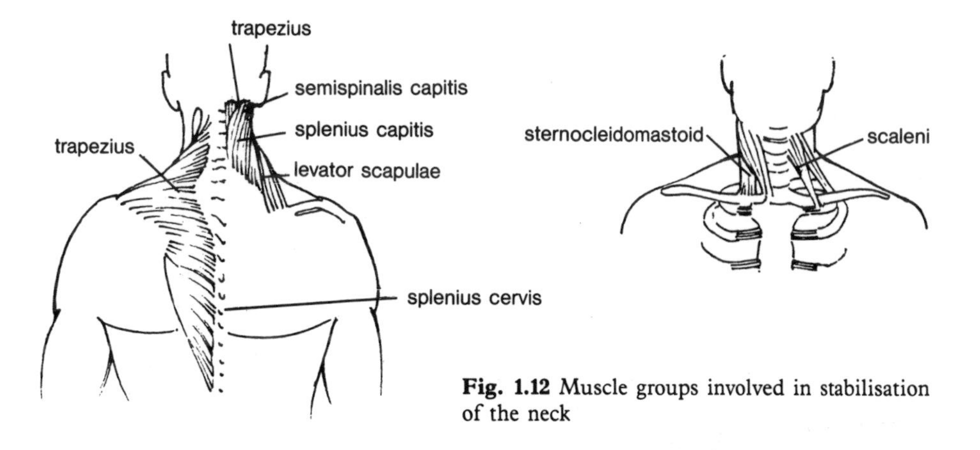

Fig. 1.12 Muscle groups involved in stabilisation of the neck

and upper (cervical) spine. The trapezius and levator scapulae also assist in stabilising this area. Neck strength in football is extremely important and will be dwelt upon at length in various sections of this text. For location of these muscle groups refer to Fig. 1.12.

Shoulder girdle and joint

The shoulder girdle consists of two pairs of bones, a clavicle (collarbone) and a scapula (shoulder blade), on each side of the upper body supported on the sternum and upper rib cage. In terms of shoulder girdle movement the major prime movers are the trapezius, the pectoralis minor, rhomboid and serratus anterior.

The shoulder joint is formed by the upper arm bone (known as the humerus) which is ball shaped, joining into the circular socket of the scapula.

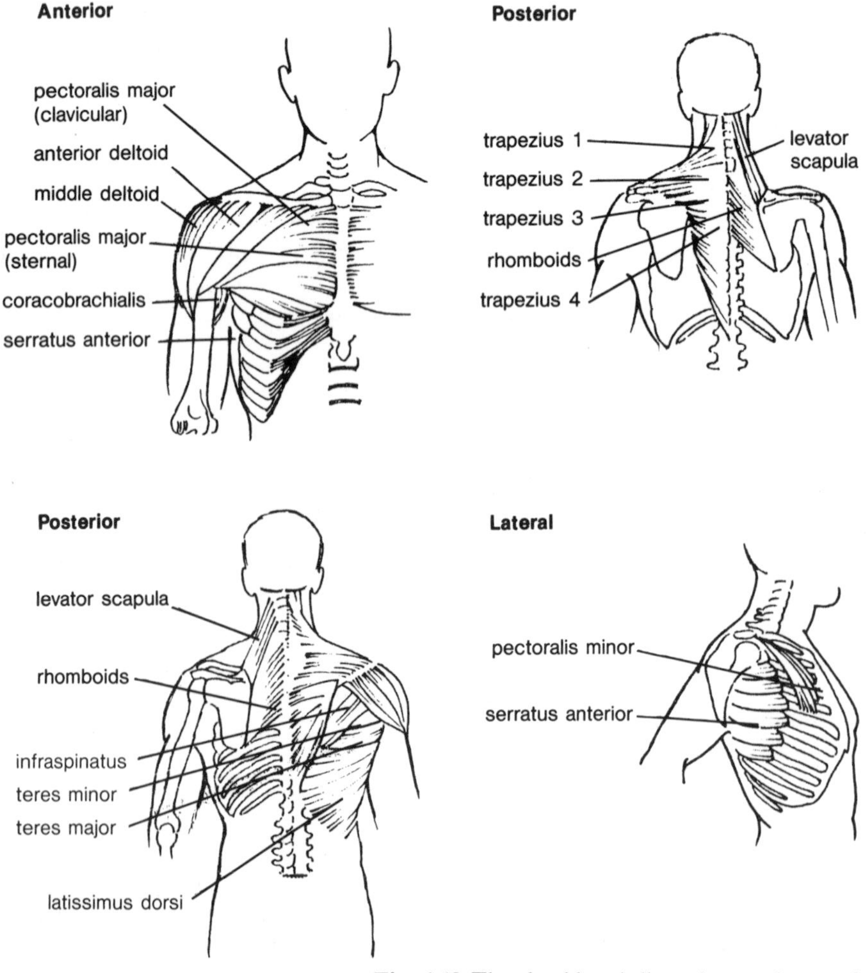

Fig. 1.13 The shoulder girdle and musculature of the shoulder joint

The shoulder joint is very mobile and the least stable of the large joints.

This ball and socket joint enables the shoulder joint to move in a multitude of directions. The deltoid muscle, which is virtually like a cap on the shoulder joint (and has three sections—anterior, lateral and posterior), is a major prime mover in many shoulder movements.

Another important prime mover is the latissimus dorsi muscle, located in the upper lateral part of the back. It is this muscle that gives bodybuilders that V shape when viewed from the front or back and it is involved in movements such as chinning the bar, rowing and swimming. The pectoralis major (the largest chest muscle) is also a shoulder joint prime mover and is prominent in the performance of push ups, an exercise known to everybody.

While there are a number of small muscles involved in assisting the prime movers of the shoulder, four small muscles known as the 'rotator cuff' group (supraspinatus, infraspinatus, subscapularis and teres minor) play an important part in shoulder movement, particularly the action of throwing an object. This group of muscles is located near the scapula. Also the tendons of the rotator cuff group assist in stabilising the shoulder joint, regardless of whether the muscles are performing any other task. It should also be understood that in all arm movements in sport there is interaction between the shoulder girdle and shoulder joint.

It is important for football players to strengthen all muscles involved in the shoulder area as these joints are the subject of much stress, both in attack and defence. Furthermore, the shoulder joint is very mobile and the least stable of the large joints. Fig. 1.13 illustrates shoulder girdle and joint musculature.

Elbow joint

The elbow joint is generally referred to as a hinge joint, and as such moves in one plane of flexion and extension. The major prime movers for arm flexion (bending of the arm) are the biceps, brachialis and brachioradialis. The biceps muscle is familiar to all and located at the front of the upper arm. The brachialis is situated near the elbow. The brachioradialis is a relatively large muscle positioned on the outer border of the forearm and gives rise to the rounded contour from elbow to base of thumb. This group of muscles is referred to collectively as the arm flexors.

Arm extension (straightening of the arm) is controlled by the triceps muscle, a three headed muscle located at the rear of the upper arm.

Wrist joint

There are many muscles involved in the control of the wrist, hand and fingers. For the purpose of this text they can be grouped under the general heading of wrist and finger flexors and extensors. All exercises using the hands as a connecting link help strengthen the wrist joint and surrounding musculature irrespective of the major purpose of the movement. This is especially so in multiple joint, multi muscle group exercises.

2. Strength, Power and Speed

The harder I work the luckier I become!

In order to understand the concepts of strength and power and their relationship to speed, let us examine in simplified form the structure and function of skeletal muscle and the factors influencing strength, power and speed.

Skeletal muscle structure and function

Muscle fibres have the ability to shorten or lengthen under tension.

Skeletal muscle is composed of many bundles of muscle fibres (see Fig. 2.1). Within a single muscle great variation exists in both size and number of muscle fibres, with the number of fibres varying from one individual to another. Since it is generally accepted that training does not increase the number of muscle fibres, the more fibres you are born with the greater will be your potential for gaining muscle strength and mass.

The nervous system and muscle movement

Muscle fibre shortening is known as concentric contraction.

Skeletal muscle fibres and indeed the muscle itself are under the control of the central nervous system, i.e. the brain in conjunction with various sensory mechanisms of the nervous system.

These muscle fibres have the ability to shorten or lengthen when under tension. A simple example of a muscle shortening under tension is when a person takes a barbell or dumbell and curls it to the shoulder/chest area, i.e. bending the arm. In this particular instance the muscle fibres of the arm flexors shorten as the weight is elevated. This is known as a concentric contraction.

Muscle fibre lengthening is known as eccentric contraction.

When the same weight is slowly lowered down to the original starting position the fibres of the arm flexors are lengthening under tension and this is referred to as an eccentric contraction. However if the amount of resistance to this arm movement is increased to the point where the arm flexors are applying maximum tension and no movement takes place, this type of contraction is known as static or isometric. Older readers may recall a form of fad training that was popular in the late sixties known

Skeletal muscles consist of many fibres arranged in bundles.

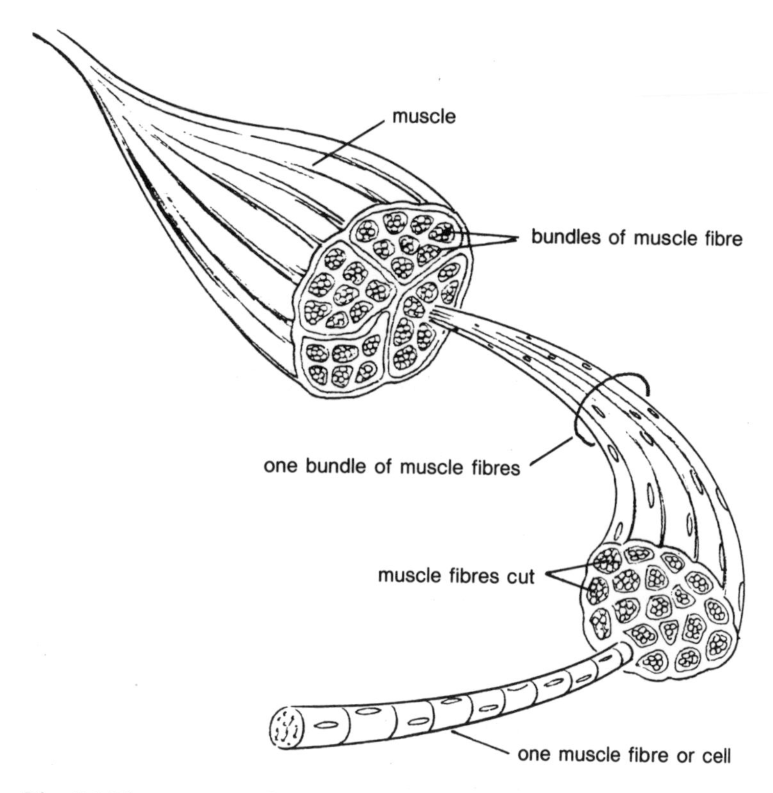

Fig. 2.1 The structure of skeletal muscle

as isometric training, which basically involved maximal pulling or pushing against an immoveable object (bar, doorway etc.) for brief periods of time.

As a point of interest most people can exert about 15% more force isometrically and 30/40% more eccentrically than they can concentrically. Indeed the practice of utilising supramaximal eccentric contractions (using resistance in exercises that is too heavy to reverse via concentric contraction—the exerciser strongly resists the 'lowering' movement and is then assisted to the commencing position by a training partner) is an advanced form of strength training.

In the abovementioned example of a person curling a bar the number of muscle fibres recruited to lift the weight depends to a large degree upon how heavy it is. The heavier the load generally the greater the number of muscle fibres recruited to lift it. Rate of frequency of muscle fibre recruitment is also a factor. This ability to maximally recruit muscle fibres is very important in the development of strength and power and is sometimes referred to as neuromuscular efficiency. It is also known as intra muscle coordination. This is not to be confused with inter muscle coordination, which is basically the ability of various muscle groups to adopt a specific pattern of synchronisation. Both intra and inter muscle coordination play a major part in skill and power development. These mechanisms can be developed by appropriate training, however genetics also plays a considerable part in ultimate ability.

Muscle fibre types

A most important factor in strength, power and speed development is muscle fibre types. Skeletal muscle is generally divided into two basic categories, sometimes referred to as red or white fibres. Another more descriptive and accurate term is slow twitch (Type I—red) and fast twitch (Type II—white). There are a number of varieties of fast twitch fibres. Some generate large tension rapidly but fatigue quickly (generally referred to as Type IIb). Others are more resistant to fatigue and are 'intermediate' type fibres. Slow twitch fibres generate a lower maximum tension at a slower rate but do not fatigue easily.

Slow twitch fibres are the endurance fibres.

As a general rule slow twitch fibres are preferentially recruited for endurance activities such as long distance running, cycling or swimming. This also includes lifting light weights for many repetitions. Successful endurance athletes in most instances have a predominance of slow twitch fibres in the specific muscle groups used for the activity. Fast twitch fibres are the opposite. They contract nearly three times faster than their slow twitch counterparts and are recruited (together with slow twitch) for explosive activities such as sprinting, throwing objects, jumping, and team games such as football. This greater contraction speed of fast twitch fibres becomes a major advantage to the athlete who is well endowed in this area. All other things equal he is going to have a big advantage in power over his opponents who are not so genetically fortunate. The percentage of fast twitch to slow twitch muscle fibres varies from person to person and also in different muscle groups within the same person.

Fast twitch muscle fibres are utilised for power activities.

The proportion of fast twitch to slow twitch fibres an individual possesses is genetically determined. Furthermore the weight of evidence at the present moment would indicate that it is unlikely that training can alter this situation to any great extent, although certain of the fast twitch fibres (the intermediate type), through concerted endurance training, can assume proportionally more of the slow twitch muscle fibre characteristics. Unfortunately the same does not apply in reverse.

Muscle fibre size

Another factor in how much tension can be developed in a muscle is the cross sectional size and volume of the muscle fibres. As a general rule the larger the muscle the more tension it is capable of developing.

However this can be relative. For instance if an athlete has selectively exercised a particular muscle group utilising a light resistance for many repetitions it is most likely that increases in muscle fibre size (hypertrophy) will be accentuated in the slow twitch fibres and therefore will not make the contribution to increased strength and power that appearance would suggest.

A typical example of this is that in the sport of bodybuilding it is not uncommon to find two competitors with similar physical characteristics who have significantly different strength levels. In most instances the major

HFC
1
HFC FINANC
8
VANCE
0

CRISPS

Increase muscle size via fast twitch fibre development.

reason for this is that the weaker person has trained predominantly on higher repetitions against a lighter resistance whereas the stronger person has followed a more varied program in which both types of muscle fibre receive equal attention.

Indeed a study conducted in Sweden in 1982 showed a lack of fast twitch muscle fibre hypertrophy in bodybuilders whose work out sets consisted of eight to twenty repetitions. On the contrary, power lifters whose workout sets were high in weight and low in repetitions had significantly larger fast twitch fibres. This evidence supports empirical observations that (a) heavier resistance for lesser repetitions is preferable for maximising strength and (b) that muscle hypertrophy is not always a true reflection of strength and power.

You can become stronger without increasing muscle size.

In terms of muscle size and strength, it is important to understand that strength development can be increased in an ongoing manner with minimal muscle size gain (hypertrophy). This is born out by the fact that it is quite common to observe Olympic weightlifters, upon reaching physical maturity, compete in the same bodyweight class for a number of years and yet continue to improve their strength/power levels. In this instance the major process involved in this progression is increased neuromuscular efficiency. However to keep matters in perspective, at elite levels of Olympic weightlifting the heavier the bodyweight class the greater the amount of weight lifted.

Strength can be absolute, i.e. no consideration of body size, or it can be relative—a ratio of strength to bodyweight. While an increase in maximal strength is generally accompanied by a bettering of relative strength, the concept of increased strength without bodyweight increase can be important in sports where increased size can be an impediment.

It should also be understood that when an athlete reaches a 'sticking point' (cessation of strength gains through neuromuscular efficiency) at a particular bodyweight, the major mechanism for breaking this barrier is increased muscle hypertrophy.

Genetic factors affecting strength and power development

A person's genetic potential for physical performance is determined at birth and dependent very much on the physical talents of his ancestors. Obviously all individuals are not made from the same mould. Therefore all are not capable of running at the same speed, jumping the same height, lifting identical weights or having equal skills in a particular activity.

As an individual approaches the higher levels of athletic competition a process of natural selection becomes evident: many athletes obtain a reasonable degree of success in sport but the numbers narrow as the higher levels of performance are approached. However it should be remembered that with correct training the majority of individuals are capable of

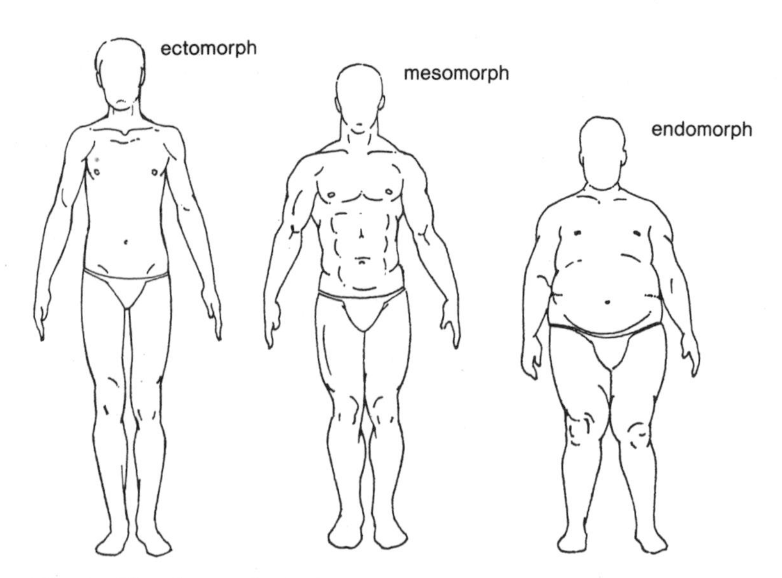

Fig. 2.2 The three major body types

Very few people develop their physical talents to the fullest extent.

considerable improvement. While each person has limitations, very few develop their talents to the fullest extent.

Let us now consider these genetic factors affecting the development of strength and power (and speed). Two factors previously discussed are muscle fibre types and neuromuscular efficiency (the ability of the nervous system to recruit muscle fibres) which is partly genetic and partly a training process. Other factors are body type, bone lengths, insertion points of muscles and their length.

Body types can be categorically placed into three broad and very general groups. These groups are known as ectomorph, mesomorph and endomorph.

Ectomorphs are characterised by fragility, small bones and little fat. They find it very difficult to gain muscle mass and strength. In sport ectomorphs excel in endurance events such as long distance running.

Mesomorphs are identified by a square body with hard, rugged and prominent musculation with little fat. The bones are large and covered with ample muscle. Mesomorphs react favourably to strength training and their favourite domain is the power sports.

Endomorphs are recognised by roundness and softness of body. A very high percentage of body fat is present. The strict endomorph has very little athletic potential for anything except inactivity and consuming large quantities of food.

Body type plays a large part in strength training.

However it should be remembered that few people fall categorically into one group, with most possessing characteristics from all body types with the accent on two types. Most elite football players are heavily oriented towards mesomorphic. Body type plays a large part in the results one can expect from strength training and the most suitable way to go about it.

Bone lengths, particularly in the legs, back and arms, play a significant part in a person's ability to overcome a resistance such as lifting weights. This varies according to the exercise, i.e. the manner in which the resistance is overcome. The physical laws of levers and bone lengths are closely related. However exercisers can take heart from the fact that very few people have poor leverage for all the various types of exercises. Also increased muscle cross section and volume can help offset unfavourable leverage through bone length.

Finally insertions of muscle and muscle length can have a positive or negative effect in resistance training. The further the insertion of the muscle from the joint the greater the advantage. Bone lengths and muscle insertions are more critical to weight lifters and throwers than to football players.

Strength and power

Strength

Strength is the ability to exert maximum force.

It is difficult to give a real definition of strength but basically it is the ability to exert maximum muscle tension (force) for a short period of time regardless of velocity of movement.

Some typical examples of strength are those exhibited in the World's Strongest Man Competition, segments of which are seen quite frequently on TCN 9 Wide World of Sport, in which contestants endeavour to lift up heavy barrels or stones, drag enormous boats up a slipway and other like activities. Breaking chains, engaging in tug-of-war, and lifting a very heavy weight slowly a minimal distance while exerting maximal force are other examples.

In regard to rugby codes, strength is important for the maintenance of scrum equilibrium. It also plays a big part in a player's ability to withstand the force of a tackle and unload the ball to support players. Strength is important in football but power, of which strength (force) is an ingredient, is even more essential.

Power

Power is the combination of force and speed.

It is sometimes referred to as speed strength and is simply the application of strength (force) with velocity (speed of movement). In a quantitative sense it is written as $P = F \times V$ or $P = F \times \frac{d}{t}$ although in a large number of sporting activities power represents force × acceleration (rate of change of velocity). Examples of this are sprinting short distances, jumping, throwing objects, striking activities etc.

Another factor in power is the resistance involved in a particular activity. For instance the resistance in Olympic weightlifting is quite substantial (and ever increasing), rowing involves considerable resistance (weight of boat and rowers, drag factors), throwing the hammer and shot is descending

Strength and power are essential ingredients of football.

the scale, while activities like tennis and golf are at the opposite end of the continuum. The greater the resistance the more force required in the 'power equation', while the less the resistance the more speed becomes the dominant (but not total) factor.

$$\uparrow P = \frac{\uparrow F \times d}{t} \qquad \uparrow P = \frac{F \times d}{t\downarrow}$$

Maximal force and speed of movement are equally important in the football 'power equation'.

In football the power situation is complex. In sprinting and agility/skill activities the major resistance is the player's bodyweight. However in skills such as tackling and breaching the defence the resistance is considerably greater. Therefore maximal force and speed of movement are equally important in the football 'power equation'.

Development of strength and power

Strength is best developed by performing a compound exercise a minimal number of repetitions with a resistance close to maximum. A compound exercise is one that involves a number of major muscles together with multiple joint action. It is also referred to as a core movement or total body exercise. Squatting with a weight across the shoulders is a good example of a compound/total body exercise. It creates tension in the quadriceps, hamstrings, glutes, lower back and to a lesser extent in a number of other muscle groups. The opposite to a compound exercise is a sectional movement which creates tension in a lesser number of muscle groups with minimal joint action. Relative to the above example of a compound exercise, leg extensions on a leg machine are sectional movements with the quadriceps of the leg being the major benefactor.

Why a compound exercise for maximal strength development? Simply because a number of major muscle groups working in a synchronised manner will always produce a greater overall tension than a movement involving an individual muscle group. For instance it is possible to perform

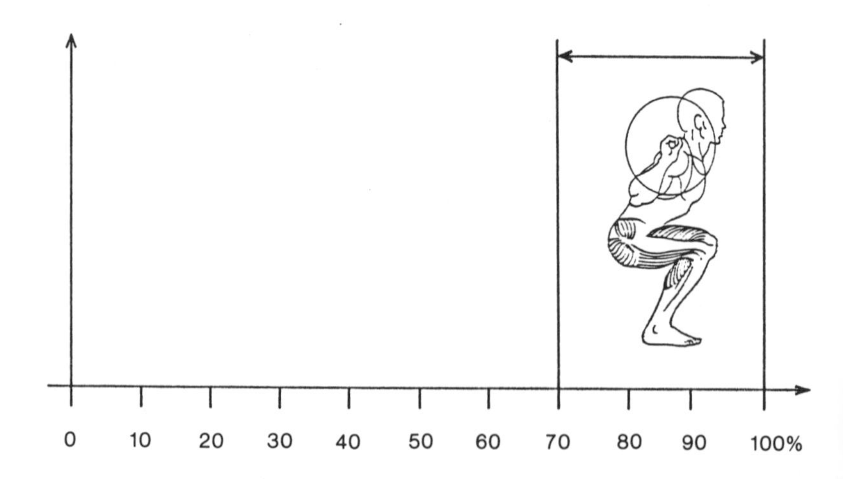

Fig. 2.3 The most effective sphere of intensity for force development

the squat exercise with much greater resistance than when performing the leg extension. Furthermore total body exercises have a positive effect on the neuromuscular mechanisms of inter and intra muscle coordination. In terms of specificity most sporting activity skills involving strength/power (including football) consist of multi muscle group synchronisation. It is therefore logical to choose exercises that operate in a similar fashion.

Power is best developed by performing multiple joint/multi muscle (compound) movements specific to one's sport with varying resistance close to maximum for a small number of repetitions in a controlled but explosive manner. Once again the rationale for utilising compound movements is the same as mentioned above for strength development.

There is a greater emphasis on speed of movement and lesser intensity (lighter resistance) in power development. However irrespective of whether the athlete is training for strength or power the 'lifting' portion of the exercise (the concentric contraction) should be performed with maximum effort i.e. to move the resistance as quickly as possible. In reality strength and power are akin to each other.

Maximal strength, as well as explosive strength, is a basic quality of power. Thus there is no conflicting influence between maximal strength and power. In other words, a high level of maximal strength has no negative influence on movement speed. Indeed, research has shown the opposite, i.e. enhancement. Empirically this is borne out by the strength levels of many of the world's best 'speed' athletes. 'Flo-Jo' Joyner, the world's fastest woman and the star of track and field at the 1986 Olympics, can squat in excess of double bodyweight. The same can be said of Australia's world champion sprint cyclist, Martin Vinnicombe, who performs multiple repetitions on 200 kg in the back squat. 1986 100-metre Australian sprint champion, Shane Naylor, is extremely powerful. The majority of professional footballers in the American National Football League also epitomise the combination of strength and speed.

Another major factor in power development is choice of exercise. Some exercises can only be performed correctly in an explosive manner. Examples are the power clean and snatch which will be discussed in greater detail at a later stage.

Strength and power can be very closely allied in the same movement. For instance squatting with a resistance close to maximum for a couple of repetitions is predominently strength development, whereas reducing the resistance to about 65/70% of maximum for the same number of repetitions would involve greater speed of execution and consequently increase the power content. At the other end of the spectrum, performing squat jumps as high and explosive as possible with light dumbells is power with the accent on speed. *It is important when planning exercises and programs for power sports to take into consideration the fact that high force and high speed exercises recruit fast twitch fibres.*

Increased strength and power enables skill to be executed more efficiently.

Finally, strength and power do not guarantee skill, but increased strength and power enable the skill to be executed more efficiently, i.e. the player can run faster, jump higher, tackle harder.

Martin Vinnicombe, 1987 World 1 km Sprint Cycle Champion—and strongman extraordinaire

Shane Naylor, 1988 Australian 100 metre sprint champion, performing repetition back squats with 175 kg

Olympic weightlifting—the epitome of speed/strength

Speed and the factors involving its development

Speed of limb movement relative to football is predominantly about sprinting and agility. It could be further defined as acceleration and agility over comparatively short distances. There are occasions when a football player is able to make a long break and run a considerable distance. However in this modern era coaches place ever increasing stress on defence, with the result that long breaks are becoming more infrequent. It is the ability to repeatedly accelerate quickly for short distances that is important in football. Speed over the first ten to fifteen metres is greatly influenced by leg strength and explosive 'jump' power.

When discussing speed development it should be remembered that speed can be improved, but only to the point of the individual's genetic potential. A slow athlete cannot become a speedster but can be trained to develop his limited ability to the fullest.

The major attack points for developing speed are neuromuscular efficiency (reaction time and starting ability), stride length and rate (which is also partly neuromuscular), together with anaerobic conditioning, i.e. the ability to be able to repeat the sprints constantly with minimum fatigue.

Increasing your stride length without reducing the rate of leg movement is an efficient way of improving speed over short distances (although there is such a thing as overstriding, mainly related to incorrect running form). Stride length is dependant upon sprinting form, leg strength and flexibility. Increased strength and power in the relevant muscle groups enable the athlete to apply more force against the ground with the pushing leg. This enhanced ground reaction force has a positive effect on stride length. Optimal stride length for each athlete is relative to height and length of leg. Top class sprinters have stride lengths ranging from seven to eight feet. Some have registered as much as nine feet.

Stride length increase and its effect on 40 metre dash time with a flying start

	Stride length		Stride rate	Metres/sec	Approx. 40 metre dash time
Original speed	2 m	×	4 steps/sec	= 8 m	5.0 sec
New Speed	2.15 m	×	4 steps/sec	= 8.6 m	4.6 sec approx.

The table listed above shows the importance of lengthening your stride. A 15 cm increase while maintaining a stride rate of four steps per second would improve speed by 60 cm per second. Over four to five seconds a player would travel 2.4 to 3.0 m further with his new stride length.

There is greater emphasis on speed in power development.

Stride rate is the sum of the time for ground contact and time in the air. Stride rate relies upon neuromuscular efficiency, favourable muscle fibre composition, good strength/weight ratio and sprinting form. Neuromuscular efficiency is the nervous and muscular system's ability to produce a rapid contraction and relaxation. This in turn is heavily influenced by a favourable ratio of fast twitch to slow twitch fibres in the relevant muscle groups. As was the case with stride length, sprinting form is also important in increased stride rate. Favourable strength/weight ratio is another factor in ultimate stride cadence via lessening the time for foot ground contact without loss of push off power. It is generally accepted that stride rate is more difficult to improve than stride length.

Activities that assist in development of stride length and frequency

Sprinting is governed by stride length and stride rate.

(a) Form training and sprint drills. Form training consists of attention to the following—arm action, body lean, knee/leg action, over/under striding, together with upper arm and neck/facial tension. Correcting major faults can cut valuable tenths of a second off a player's sprint times. There are many sprint drills that can be utilised to improve a player's sprint ability. Butt kickers, various types of bounding, pawing, pull throughs and high knee lifts are examples of such drills.

Optimal stride rate is relative to height and length of leg.

(b) Stretching. Flexibility is very important in sprinting. Chapter 5 is devoted entirely to this subject.

(c) Strength training. Chapter 3 is particularly relevant to strength training specific to sprinting. Concepts of strength and power have already been discussed in this chapter.

Increased leg and hip strength has a positive effect on stride length.

(d) Sprint loading. This means sprinting against increased resistance. There are a number of ways this can be performed. Hill sprinting, running up stadium stairs and towing a weighted object are good examples of sprint loading. For hill sprinting distances should vary from 40 to 80 metres. Towing a weighted object is best suited to 20 to 40 metres. Ensure that overall weight allows proper form and reasonable running speed. Too much weight defeats the purpose of the exercise. An approximation would be 10% of bodyweight.

(e) Plyometric activities. This subject is discussed in a later part of this chapter.

(f) Overspeed training. Activities that fall under this heading are downhill sprinting, different forms of overspeed towing and high speed stationary cycling. The major aim is to increase stride rate. While it is difficult to improve this some sprint authorities believe that overspeed training may have a positive effect.

Stride rate is the sum of the time for ground contact and the time in the air.

Downhill running is best performed on a slope not in excess of three degrees (a slight decline). If the slope is excessive body lean decreases and the athlete will contact the ground too far in front of the body. This

Stride rate is more difficult to improve than stride length.

produces a braking effect. Consequently a forceful push-off is very difficult, a situation hardly conducive to increased stride cadence. Ideally the training terrain should consist of a downhill slope of about 50 metres followed by about 20 metres of flat area. This enables the athlete to gain maximum momentum downhill and then try to hold the increased speed for 20 metres on the level surface.

Stride length is also dependant upon flexibility.

Uphill and downhill running assists speed development.

Overspeed towing has been used by some sprint coaches in an endeavour to develop both increased stride rate and length. In some instances a four station tow bar apparatus has been attached to a motor car, while in the USA a motorised device called the Sprint Master has been designed to perform the same task. Another method practised in the USA is to use a piece of surgical tubing about seven to eight metres long with a waist belt attached. The opposite end can be attached to a goal post. The idea is for the athlete to back away from the stationary attachment and stretch the tubing some twenty metres. He then sprints as fast as possible aided by the slingshot effect of the surgical tubing. The major problem with overspeed towing in Australia is the lack of suitable facilities for the majority of football players. Also there is an element of danger with this type of activity. Finally the efficacy of overspeed training is still unproven.

High speed stationary cycling may increase stride rate.

Research has indicated that high speed stationary cycling may increase stride rate. This is based on the fact that stride rate of top class male sprinters is between 4.5–5 strides per second whereas cycling cadence can be as high as 5.5–7 revolutions per second.

Body fat and stride rate

Elimination of excess body fat can have a positive effect on stride rate. Fat accumulation in muscle fibres hinders rapid contraction. Lower body fat will also improve strength/weight ratio.

Plyometrics

Plyometrics—a link in the speed strength chain.

Plyometrics is a term which became popular amongst coaches in track and field athletics in the early seventies. Originating in the Soviet bloc countries it was initially used extensively in athletics and Olympic weightlifting. Over the years it has gained world wide acceptance and is now an integral part of the training programs for all power sports, forming an important link in the speed/strength chain.

Plyometrics consists of a number of drills or exercises encompassing a rapid stretching of a muscle(s) that is undergoing eccentric stress (the fibres lengthening) followed by an equally rapid concentric contraction of that muscle (the fibres shortening) for the purpose of developing a forceful movement over a short period of time. Physiologists refer to this action as the stretch shortening cycle. The faster and more forceful the eccentric contraction then the greater and more rapid will be the concentric contraction. It is an involuntary contraction elicited by the 'stretch reflex'

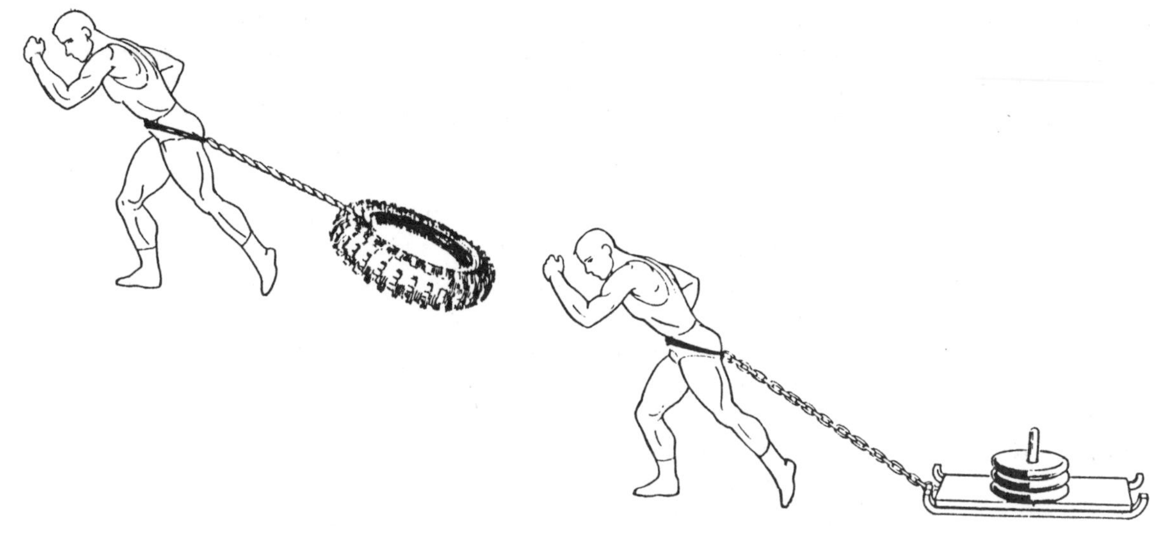

Fig. 2.4 Towing an object to develop strength for sprinting

mechanism of the muscular joint, which sends a powerful stimulus to the muscles causing them to contract faster and with more power. The loading or stretching action is sometimes called the yielding phase and the actual reflex contraction of the muscles the overcoming phase.

In a volitional contraction it takes approximately six to eight tenths of a second to achieve a maximal contraction. However in activities such as sprinting and jumping (very specific to football) foot contact time with the ground is between one tenth and two tenths of a second. Thus the key to achieving a maximally explosive push off is to have the muscles

Fig. 2.5 Towing using a car and towline produces extremely high stride rates

You can generate more power by preceding a movement with a counter movement in the opposite direction.

respond with maximal force in the shortest amount of time. This can only be done by preceding the concentric contraction with a fast forceful eccentric contraction.

In a simpler sense you can generate more power in any muscle group by first starting a movement in the opposite direction. The golf and tennis swing are examples of pre-stretching by movement in the opposite direction before the explosive swing occurs. Just try starting your golf swing from the top and see how far you hit the ball!

Examples of eccentric-concentric coupling abound in athletics. For instance in sprinting when the front foot makes contact with the ground the quadriceps of the thigh momentarily lengthens as the body moves into its lowest position and then shortens as the centre of gravity rises (as mentioned above this action takes place in between one and two tenths of a second). Similar actions take place when a footballer is accelerating, side stepping etc.

Skeletal muscle has an elastic component.

Skeletal muscle has an elastic component and, in parallel with the stretch reflex mechanism, the utilisation of this elasticity also plays a part in the stretch shortening cycle. The muscles around the active joint become loaded or coiled and the energy accumulated from the loading is switched in direction and the body is propelled in a 'spring-like' action.

Plyometrics revolves around jump activities.

In its practical applications plyometrics has many forms but in general it revolves around jump activities. For example bounding, single or double leg hops, triple jumps, jumps for height, distance or a combination of both, jumps onto and off boxes of various heights and lateral jumping are all major forms of this type of training. There are also many plyometric drills with medecine balls of a throwing and catching nature that develop the same explosive quality in the upper body that jump drills do in the lower body.

Opinion varies considerably about what type of plyometric training is suitable for different sports. However, taking into account specificity, activities that involve horizontal forces (e.g. running) would accentuate hopping/bounding movements while sports that involve vertical forces (jumping, Olympic weightlifting etc.) would emphasise various forms of depth jumps.

In view of the fact that all codes of football involve horizontal forces such as short sprints and agility, single and double leg hopping over short distances at a maximum rate is an ideal supplement to speed training. The length of the hop is secondary, rate is more important. Distance might vary from 15 to 25 metres. An alternative is 'power' hops where more emphasis is placed on height and 'hang time' than on speed. Jumps sideways over a low bench for 15 to 20 seconds are a good agility movement as is hopping (single and double leg) with constant rapid change of direction. An even more intensive drill is to sprint 15 to 20 metres and then hop rapidly on alternative single legs to exhaustion. Due to its intensive nature this drill should be the final aspect of a workout. It is not for beginners and should not be used in the initial stages of a plyometric program.

Twice a week is ideal.

Overall plyometric training should be performed twice a week in the off/pre season and once a week in the competition phase. Where possible this activity should be linked with sprint training. In the off season endeavour to perform plyometrics on alternate days to strength training. If for some reason plyometrics are performed on the same day as strength training, separate them by at least three to four hours. For maximal effect from this mode of training the neuromuscular system should be in a non fatigued state.

Jumping ability and plyometrics

Vertical jumping is dependant upon strength and speed.

Maximisation of vertical jumping ability is very important in Australian Rules football and to a lesser extent in rugby codes.

In the kinesiology of jumping the lower leg, thighs, hip/back extensors and flexors are all heavily involved in both a concentric and eccentric manner—the going up and all important coming down (shock absorption).

Indeed vertical jumping is a total body movement relying on speed, strength and power to attain maximal results. It is very much a plyometric action in so far as there is a pre-stretching or lengthening (in a short explosive manner) of muscles prior to contraction. This is borne out by the fact that (a) the performer who can step into the take off position rather than execute the jump from a stationary position will jump higher and (b) when performing the 'vertical jump and reach test' a pre-stretch or dip will result in a higher mark than when the movement commences from a static position.

Taking into consideration the above facts, the three major factors in increasing jumping ability are (a) practising jumping itself, (b) strengthening the muscles involved by specific total body movements such as squats, dumbell squat jumps and power cleans, (c) jump specific plyometrics—depth jumping.

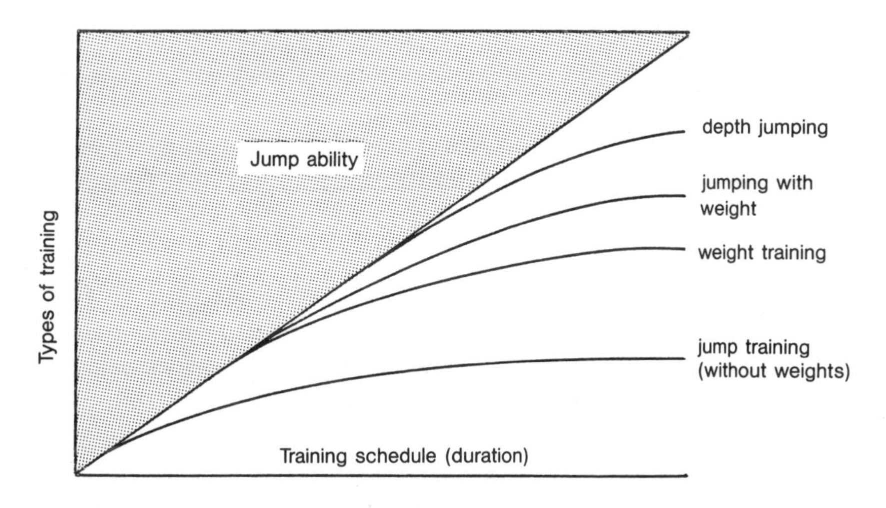

Fig. 2.6 Exercises to maximise jumping ability

Depth jumps

Heights of 0.8 to 1.1 metres are most effective for depth jumps.

Depth jumps can take various forms. Essentially they entail stepping off a box of variable heights and either rebounding upwards or onto other box/boxes of equal or lesser height. Research in the USSR would indicate that a height of 0.8 to 1.1 metres is the most effective. Other studies have indicated that heights from 0.5 to 2(!) metres have also been effective in increasing muscular strength and neural efficiency.

Professor D. Schmidtbleicher of Frankfurt University, a doyen of strength training research, is firmly of the opinion that in the past athletes have utilised excessive heights in depth jumps. This has resulted in both lessening their adaptive efficiency and increasing the likelihood of musculoskeletal trauma (short and long term). He recommends that athletes should restrict height of depth jumps to ball of foot contact only, i.e. if heels contact the jumping surface the height is excessive. This height will vary amongst athletes, and also with training experience. Height should be increased as stretch reflex mechanism improves.

Another system in favour with some coaches is to use the vertical jump test as a guide. The height that an athlete can reach by jumping off a particular height of the box should correlate with his vertical jump test. In other words when the height of the box is such that the jump height equals the vertical jump test height, then that is the approximate training height. As vertical jump test height improves, the depth jump height should be reappraised.

Some guidelines for correct performance of plyometrics

1. The training surface should be resilient without being so soft that it absorbs all the forces upon landing. Grass is a suitable surface for horizontal jumping and is readily available. Depth jumping is usually performed indoors and a firm rubber surface is ideal.

It is the rate of stretch that is important not the length.

2. It is the rate of eccentric stretch that is most important not the length. In other words flexion of the hips in the landing position should not be excessive.

3. It is important to thoroughly warm up and stretch before engaging in plyometric activities.

Don't forget to warm up and stretch.

4. At all times endeavour to land on the balls of the feet.

5. In plyometrics more is not better, aim at quality work.

6. Plyometrics, particularly depth jumping, should not be done by athletes who have any history of orthopaedic problems in the knees, ankles or lower back.

Ground contact should be as short as possible.

7. Endeavour to keep an upright position on landing i.e. minimal waist sag.

8. Ground contact should be as short as possible. This is important and the exerciser should think 'landing on hot coals' or 'light quick feet'.

As vertical jump height improves reappraise depth jump height.

Fig. 2.7 Depth jumps

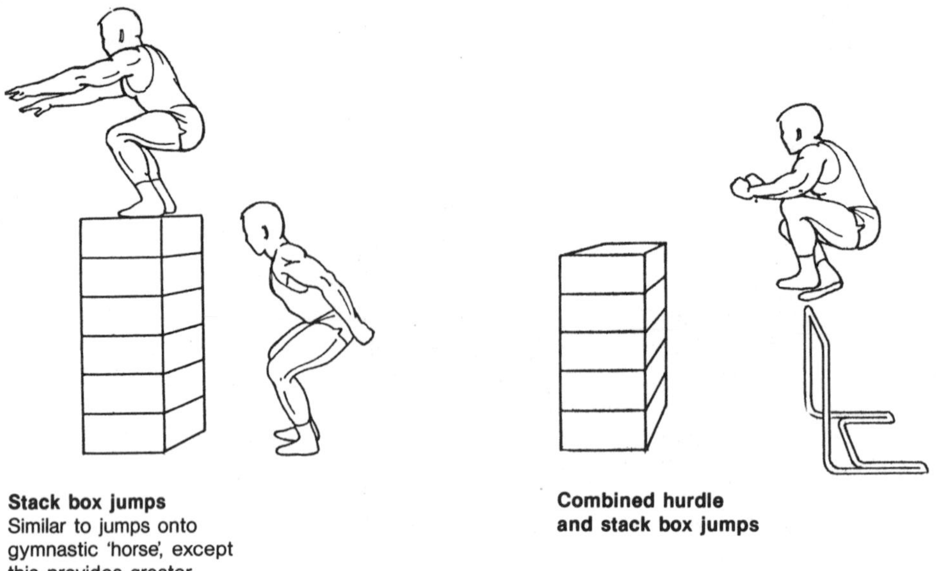

Stack box jumps
Similar to jumps onto gymnastic 'horse', except this provides greater adjustability

Combined hurdle and stack box jumps

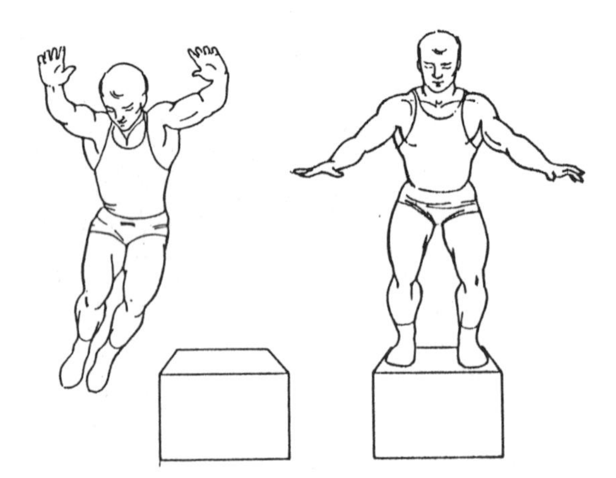

Lateral box jump
An agility/vertical force movement

Combination depth jumps

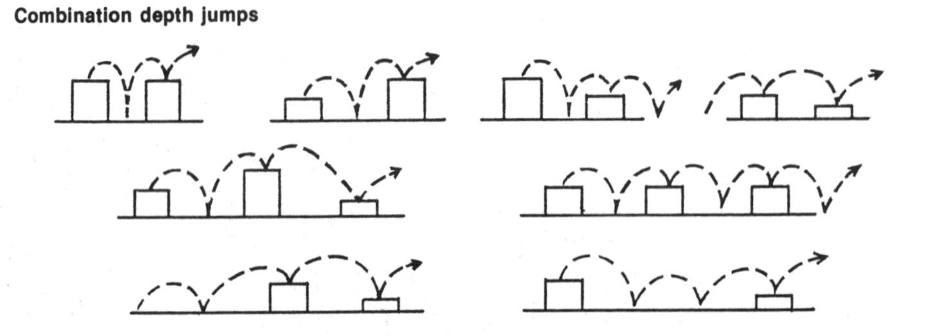

Fig. 2.8 More depth jumps

9. For continuity of progress use the overload principle. However proceed with caution. It should be kept in mind that plyometric training is very intense with the large forces developed placing great demand on the hip, knee, lower back and ankle joint, so progression should be carefully monitored. Begin with a small number of jumps and slowly build up the volume and intensity. Two legged movements should be used for a reasonable period of time before proceeding to single leg. Squat jumps, tuck jumps, box jumps etc. should be used as a lead up to depth jumps. There should be ample recovery time between each series (set) of jumps to allow complete recovery of the neural system (three to five minutes).

10. *Plyometric training should be preceded by and carried out in parallel with a strength training program.* Soviet authorities recommend that leg strength should be in the range of one and a half to double bodyweight back squat before commencing this type of training. This figure may be unreasonable and hazardous for youngsters. A more equitable figure for this group would be around bodyweight. The key to prescribing plyometric training for youngsters is lower intensity and fewer repetitions. Taking into consideration the extreme biomechanical loading of the musculoskeletal system when performing plyometrics and the fact that young athletes are more prone to musculoskeletal trauma, extreme care should be taken with the younger person. They should begin with simple low intensity movements in combination with a sound strength training program. A solid base of strength should be established as a precursor before youngsters attempt depth jump related activities.

Keep it simple for youngsters.

1st year plyometric program

Beginning phase (pre-season)			*Intermediate phase* (pre-season preparatory)			*In-season* ***		
Age	*Base of Strength* *	*Number of Foot Contacts* **	*Age*	*Base of Strength*	*Number of Foot Contacts*	*Age*	*Base of Strength*	*Number of Foot Contacts*
12–15	50%	40 (per session)	12–15	50%	70	12–15	50%	30
15–18	100%	50	15–18	100%	85	15–18	100%	40
18+	150%	60	18+	150%	100	18+	150%	50

2nd year plyometric program

Intermediate phase (pre-season)			*Advanced phase* (pre-season preparatory)			*In-season*		
Age	*Base of Strength*	*Number of Foot Contacts*	*Age*	*Base of Strength*	*Number of Foot Contacts*	*Age*	*Base of Strength*	*Number of Foot Contacts*
12–15	50%	70	12–15	50%	100	12–15	50%	50
15–18	100%	85	15–18	100%	125	15–18	100%	60
18+	150%	100	18+	150%	150	18+	150%	70

* Base of strength the percent of the athlete's bodyweight that he/she is able to do in a one repetition maximum squat.

** One jump counts as one foot contact, i.e. an in-depth jump is one foot contact, a double leg hop is one, two double leg hops are two foot contacts and a triple jump is two foot contacts.

*** Plyometrics are to be done once a week in-season.

The plyometric table above was compiled by American plyometric authority Dr R. Chu. It is based on foot contacts per session and can be interpreted in a number of ways. For instance sixty foot contacts per session could be two exercises of thirty foot contacts or three of twenty. The thirty contacts could be three sets (groups) of ten. These variables are left to the discretion of the coach/athlete and are subject to other factors such as type and intensity of exercise. What is important with Chu's method is a gradual overload over a two year period.

Fig. 2.9 Skipping drill

1. Start relaxed with one foot in front of the other.
2. From the back leg, drive off and make a short skip.
3. With the opposite leg drive knees to chest and arms into air.
4. On landing repeat the action.
5. A pattern of right-right/step/left-left/step/right-right develops.

Fig. 2.10 Double leg bound drill

1. Start with a half squat, arms at side and shoulders forward.
2. Jump upwards and at the same time forward while thrusting the arms high into the air.
3. Try to achieve maximum distance as well as height.
4. On landing, start sequence again.

Fig. 2.11 Alternate leg bound drill
1. Start with one foot slightly ahead of the other.
2. Initiate a step with the back foot pushing off.
3. Drive the knee of the back foot to the chest while driving the arms into the air, upwards and backwards.
4. Gain as much height and distance as possible.
5. With the driving foot reach out as far as possible just prior to landing.
6. Start again with the opposite foot leading—this comes naturally after landing on the lead leg.

Fig. 2.12 Squat jump drill
1. Start in a relaxed upright position, with the hands behind the head.
2. Drop quickly to a half squat position and then quickly stop this and drive upwards in an explosive fashion.
3. Jump as high as possible. Keep the hands behind the head as this will maximise the involvement of the legs and hips
4. On landing repeat the sequence.

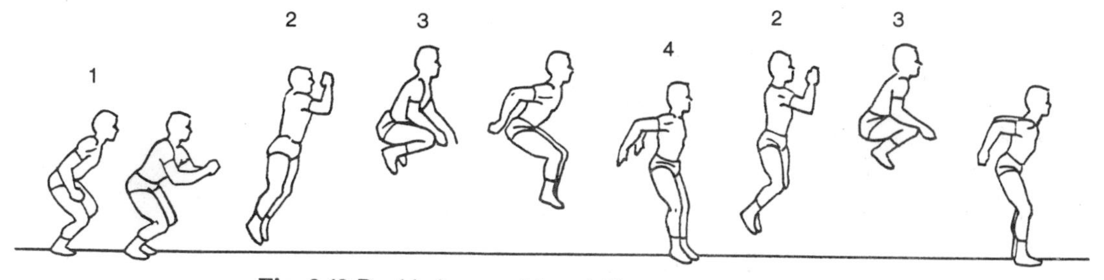

Fig. 2.13 Double leg speed hop drill
1. Start in a relaxed upright position, arms at side bent at ninety degrees.
2. Jump as high as possible, driving arm upwards.
3. Bring the legs up under the buttocks in a flexed position with knees.
4. On landing repeat the sequence.
5. Work as rapidly as possible.

Fig. 2.14 Single leg speed hop drill
1. In this exercise one leg is held in a flexed position.
2. Jump as high as possible bringing the knee forward and arms upward.
3. Flex the jumping leg so that it comes up under the buttocks.
4. Land on the same leg as the takeoff leg.
5. Repeat the sequence.

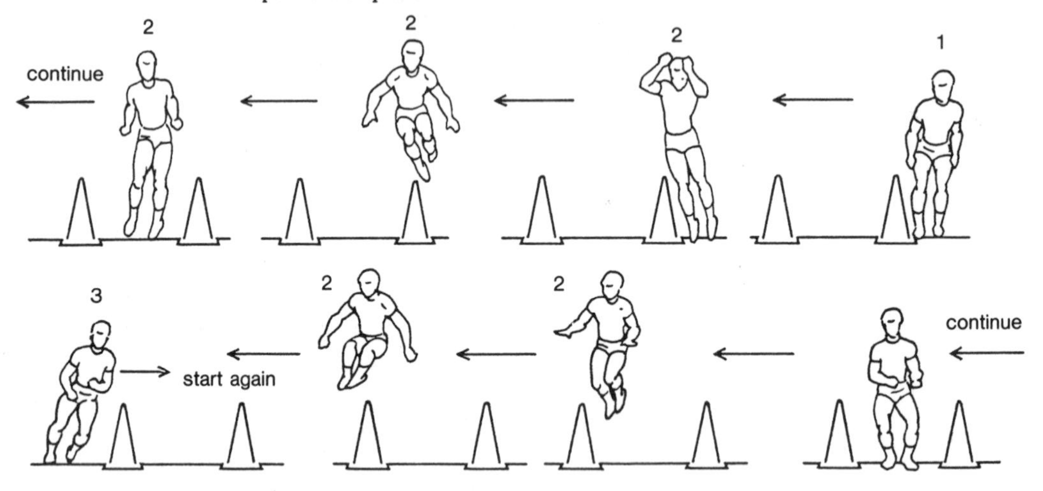

Fig. 2.15 Side hop drill
1. With the cones 1 metre apart, start at the outside of one cone in a relaxed upright position, feet together and arms ready at the side.
2. Jump sideways over the first cone using the arms to drive upwards, and then over the second cone.
3. Without stopping, change direction and go back over the cones in the opposite direction.
4. Continue this sequence.

Diagrams are adapted from Radcliffe and Farentinos (1985), pp.30–77.

Fig. 2.16 Plyometric drills with a medicine ball

3. The Origin of Power and 'The Big Two'

Speed is a fast expression of strength.

The origin of power is the legs and hips.

While total body development is an important concept of strength training, the origin of power (the power zone) in football is unquestionably the lower body (i.e. legs, hips, abdominals and lower back). It is these major muscle groups, the largest and most powerful in the body, that generate the forces needed to propel the body faster, jump higher, tackle harder, take evasive action and 'bust the defence'.

This power zone could be likened to a multi stage rocket. The initial and most powerful thrust to overcome inertia and blast off resembles the muscle tension generated in the lower body and mid torso. To maintain this initial momentum the less powerful stages of the missile come into play. Here again the smaller and less forceful muscle groups adopt a similar role for the continuity of momentum. This transfer of forces resembles a chain reaction or summation of forces.

The two most effective power exercises are power cleans and squats.

In view of the importance of hip and leg power let us now examine the productive way to develop this commodity. *The two most effective exercises for the development of the power zone are the squat and power clean.* These exercises are multiple joint/multi muscle group movements or total body exercises/core movements.

'The big two' should be the basis of all strength programs for football.

Together these two movements work the major muscle groups of the power zone in a controlled, coordinated and explosive manner with the accent on both strength and speed. Taking into consideration the fact that in terms of biomechanical specificity there is an excellent transfer of strength and power to the power skills of football, 'the big two' should be the basis of every football player's strength training program.

The squat

Most strength training authorities consider the back squat to be the 'king of exercises'. The rationale for this is based on the fact that:

(a) A great amount of muscle mass is involved in the performance of this exercise and as such it is *numero uno* for absolute strength development in the power zone. Furthermore squats have an excellent effect on muscle hypertrophy when higher repetitions (6–10) are utilised. The squat also places a high stress on the musculoskeletal system, causing the body to adapt in a positive manner in regard to tendon/ligament strength and bone density.

(b) Squats are the best quadricep exercise and develop the legs very appropriately for the demands of running sports such as football. Squatting is also an excellent strengthener of the hip extensors.

(c) Squats also uniquely prepare the quadriceps for eccentric contractions involved in the deceleration required in sprinting and jumping (refer to Chapter 2—Plyometrics), serving primarily to absorb the forces of impact. Weak quadriceps contribute significantly to knee injuries because of their inability to effectively decelerate the body in running and jumping. The importance of eccentric training on these muscles is vital.

However in spite of their great value, squats are sometimes maligned by ill-informed coaches and exercise physiologists. The major points of criticism are:

(a) that squats are injurious to the knee and lower back and
(b) they have some mystical ability to hamper running speed.

Let us examine these misconceptions and place them in a proper perspective.

Fallacy 1

Squats assist in the protection of the knee joint.

Musculature around the knee joint is the second line of defence.

If squats are performed in a correct manner they are no more likely to cause injury than any other strength training exercise. Indeed they assist in the protection of the knee joint. Even though the knee ligaments are considered to be the first line of defence against injury, they are dependent upon the strength of musculature which crosses the knee joint for protection when the stresses against the knee joint are excessive and beyond the ability of the ligaments to overcome—a situation that is quite prevalent in football.

Over the last two decades there have been a number of studies by exercise physiologists on the squat and its effect on the knee joint. One particular study by a Dr K. Klein in the sixties indicated that squats caused unstable knee ligaments and were therefore harmful to the knee joint. This study has been quoted and perpetuated by well meaning but ill-informed physicians, coaches and trainers etc.

However Klein's study had several flaws. One was the method of assessing the knee ligament stability. Also when Klein was making his assessment of ligament stability he had prior knowledge of whether the subject was in the squat or non squat group. Such a situation could lead to 'self fulfilling prophesies', i.e. subconsciously arriving at a preconceived result. Furthermore the majority of the subjects in the squat group were competitive weightlifters who, as well as squatting, had performed squat cleans and snatches for a number of years. These two movements not only involve extensive hyperflexion of the knee, but are also very ballistic in their execution.

Since this study there have been a number of others whose conclusions have repudiated Klein's findings. Recently R. Herrick MD, FACSM, M. Stone PhD and S. Herrick conducted a study of biometric data of some two hundred powerlifters and Olympic weightlifters. In addition a poll of members of the American Orthopaedic Society of Sports Medicine and the American College of Sports Medicine was carried out. The conclusion was that squats with consequential weight resistance, *when performed correctly*, are not only 'safe', but are a significant deterrent to knee injuries, and in some circumstances squats even had a positive effect on knee rehabilitation.

Incorrect squat technique can cause injury.

Another factor to emerge from the abovementioned study is that in the relatively few instances of training induced knee pain from squatting the major causes were (a) inadequate warm up and/or stretching (b) improper technique (c) trying out untested new techniques and (d) maximum single efforts, usually in competition, far exceeding anything previously attempted in training.

If the recommendations of this text are adhered to all four factors will be eliminated.

What is correct squat technique?

1. Bar resting comfortably across upper shoulder area. Initially it is advisable to use a towel around the centre of the bar as a pad to prevent discomfort.

2. Lower and upper back are taut and in an erect position, head upright. Feet spacing slightly wider than shoulders with toes pointing slightly outwards.

Never hold breath between repetitions.

3. Inhale just prior to commencing the movement, hold breath during the exertion and exhale at or just before completion of the exercise. Never hold breath between repetitions of an exercise. This method of breathing should be used for all exercises in this text. By holding your breath during exertions, you 'fix' the rib cage (i.e. hold it in one position). The rib cage is a platform on which many muscles pull, and it is inadvisable to have it moving while your muscles are working vigorously.

Avoid descending rapidly and bouncing upwards in a ballistic manner.

4. Descend with minimal velocity to a position where thighs are approximately parallel to the floor with knees directly forward over the middle of the forefoot i.e. no inward or outward rotation on descent (or for that matter when ascending). When low position has been reached drive up vigorously back to starting position. *Avoid descending with rapidity and bouncing out of low position in a ballistic manner.*

Endeavour to keep the back as close to vertical as possible when squatting.

5. Do not bend forward while ascending or descending. Endeavour to keep the back as close to vertical as possible with hips under the bar. 'Giving' to the bar and bending forward can cause injury to the lower back.

Fallacy 2

Squats retard running speed! This is utter nonsense. As mentioned previously absolute hip and leg strength is very much a part of running faster. To reiterate, the major factors in speed and acceleration are strength and power, favourable muscle fibre composition and the ability to recruit it (neuromuscular efficiency), good running technique, flexibility and a favourable power/weight ratio.

These factors govern maximal stride length and cadence. Large ground force reaction plays a major part in stride length and in turn squats play an important part in developing this force. What is also important is that the abovementioned factors governing speed are all trained in parallel. At different times of the year (i.e. the off season, pre season, competition) some factors may be accentuated more than others but *never totally neglected.*

Strong legs are a prerequisite for speed production.

In terms of leg strength, speed and their relevance to football the author would like to make this final point—many of the world's fastest sprinters are capable of squatting 150 kg to 200 kg at bodyweights ranging from 75 to 85 kg. This reflects extremely good strength/weight ratio (relative strength), an important factor in acceleration. However it should be understood that the author is not inferring that massive leg strength is the only criterion for speed/acceleration. Indeed many other factors are involved, and there have been a considerable number of well performed sprinters who were not particularly strong in the legs in a squatting sense. What is inferred is that strong legs do play a part in speed production. Also in body contact sports such as football the body is subjected to multiple external forces: therefore squats should be a high priority movement in all strength training programs for football. Ultimate strength levels achieved will be dependent on (a) frequency, volume and intensity of training and (b) genetic factors such as physiological profile.

Front squats

Another variation of squats is the front squat, where the bar is supported across the shoulders and clavicles during the performance of the movement. Except in special circumstances, this variation is best left out of the football player's strength training inventory.

There are two reasons for this. Firstly to perform the movement correctly requires a degree of ankle and wrist flexibility not always present in football players. Small weight plates or a 3 cm block under the heels of the exerciser may assist in lack of ankle flexibility and is a practice that can be utilised in back squats when the same problem is present. However there is no easy answer to supporting the bar at the chest. Indeed when flexibility is lacking in this area supporting the bar can be quite painful and only relatively light weights can be used.

Secondly, compared to the back squat, there is a greater isolation of the quadriceps, with a lessening of involvement of the hip extensors. Also the exerciser is capable of handling much greater loads in the back squat, an essential factor in maximising strength development.

Some other aspects of leg training

Combine back squats with bench step ups for total development.

While the virtues of squatting have been extolled, it should be remembered that there are other leg exercises that have a part to play in total leg development. Stepping up and down off a bench with hand held dumbells or bar on the shoulders is a meritorious exercise, as are squat jumps with light dumbells with the accent on upward explosion. Indeed either of these two exercises combines well with back squats, providing a speed/strength effect. Leg pressing on various machines is a reasonable alternative to squatting for both variation and when injury precludes squatting.

Squatting and power cleans have a positive effect on hamstring strength.

Hamstring strength plays a big part in sprinting (and is involved in protection of the knee joint) and some individuals may need to selectively strengthen this muscle group. Indeed 'pulled' hamstring muscles are an injury often encountered in football. Therefore various forms of leg curls have a part to play in balanced leg development (although squatting and power cleans also have a positive effect on the hip extensors).

There will be times when a player has sustained 'impact' knee damage during a game. Under some circumstances extensive surgery may be required. The use of squats during recuperation from injury may be inadvisable. When faced with knee injuries players must be guided by their physician or physiotherapist as to the appropriate form of rehabilitation.

A small percentage of the population may suffer from some genetic malformation of the knee that precludes intense leg training. However

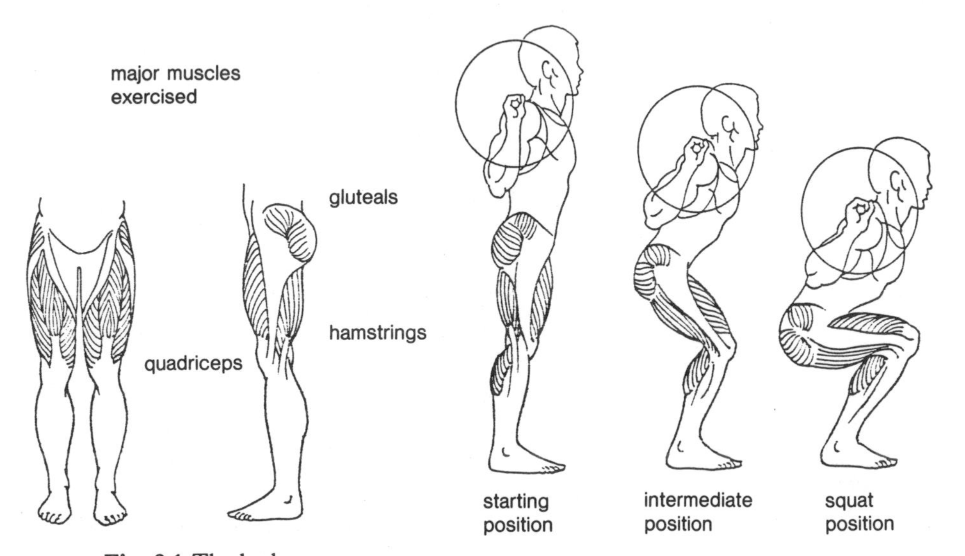

Fig. 3.1 The back squat

in this situation the same persons should give serious consideration as to whether they are suited to the rigours of body contact football.

Safety aspects of squatting

Utilise 'catchers' or 'spotters'.

Endeavour to train with partners when squatting so that they can act as 'catchers' or 'spotters' should difficulties occur.

Always face towards the squat racks so that the exerciser backs out at the commencement and walks in at the finish (when fatigued).

When squatting back out and walk in.

Don't try for that extra repetition that might not be there when training solo. If caught in the low position and unable to rise tip the bar off the back of the shoulders. It might damage the floor but the exerciser should emerge unscathed. *Don't bend forward and try to tip the bar forwards in front of the body.* This could have disastrous consequences for the neck and lower back.

Power clean

Power cleans are a total body power developer.

The other member of the 'big two', the power clean, is even more of a total body movement than the squat. Not only does it involve the lower body but also the upper back, shoulders and arms. Furthermore it can only be performed correctly in an explosive manner and the total body multiple joint/multi muscle group nature of the movement develops power in such a fashion that it has excellent transfer to the power skills of football.

Moreover, the power clean requires an athlete to exert large multiple muscle group forces while in a standing position and, together with the speed of movement involved, this develops balance and muscle coordination (a part of neural efficiency) as well as power.

The squat, depending on repetitions and resistance, can be used either as a strength movement and/or muscle builder. However the power clean has very little effect on increased muscle size and is very much a neural system exercise involving muscle fibre recruitment. Also because of the multiple muscle group involvement it is an excellent station for circuit training. Higher repetitions induce considerable stress in the cardio-pulmonary system.

Power cleans should be performed on an Olympic weightlifting bar.

To derive maximal benefit from this exercise and minimise injury risk, it is essential to learn how to perform the movement correctly. This particularly applies to the final receiving position of the weight bar, as a common fault known as 'lean back' can cause lower back strain. To avoid incorrect technique it is advisable to perform this exercise on an Olympic weightlifting bar with matching weights.

A compatible alternative is the power snatch.

A compatible alternative to the power clean is the power snatch, which is also a total body 'explosive' movement exercising similar muscle groups to the power clean. Indeed the technique for performance is almost identical, the major differences being that a wider hand spacing is adopted and the bar is elevated to arm's length as against shoulder level in the power clean. These two factors also mean that less weight can be elevated compared to the power clean.

Power clean—key performance points

There are four key positions in the correct execution of this movement. They are clearly illustrated in Fig. 3.2 and the sequence photos on page 55.

Key position 1 (KP 1)

This is the starting position and it is essential that the following points be observed:

• The bar is grasped with a shoulder width pronated grip i.e. the palms of the hand facing down. In the case of the power snatch the grip width would be approximately two hand spans wider on each side.

Keep the lower back flat and taut.

• Shoulders should be slightly over the bar, with a taut flat back, arms are straight and elbows pointing along bar. Head is in such a position that eyes are looking forward and slightly downwards.

• Hips are slightly higher than the knees with the back forming a 45°/60° angle with the horizontal (training surface). This angle is dependant upon skeletal bone lengths i.e. back and legs.

• The feet are flat on the floor about shoulder width apart with toes pointing slightly outwards. The balance should be centred over the entire foot with bar resting lightly against the shins.

The major problem for novices in assuming the correct starting position is keeping the lower back flat and taut. What happens in many instances is the novice adopts a rounded or 'banana style' lower back position. This should be corrected immediately. One way to attack this problem is to have the athlete stand erect, bar against the shins. Posterior should be jutted slightly rearward and knees moderately bent with a taut flat back (an easy position to assume). Breathe in and elevate chest, then slowly lower the body over the bar by bending the knees. Once the exerciser has done this a few times the starting position will become automatic. Some athletes master this aspect almost instantly while others take a little time to adjust.

The novice should spend the first couple of weeks mastering technique.

Key position 2 (KP 2)

The bar is close to the knees and at knee height with back and shoulders identical to floor position. Arms are still straight. Lower back flat and taut. This position is attained by simply partly straightening the legs (i.e. pushing against the floor). In the transition of the bar from the floor to knee height the largest and most powerful muscles of the body, the legs and hips, are brought into play to overcome the inertia of the barbell. The bar remains close to the shins in the transition from KP 1 to 2, moving

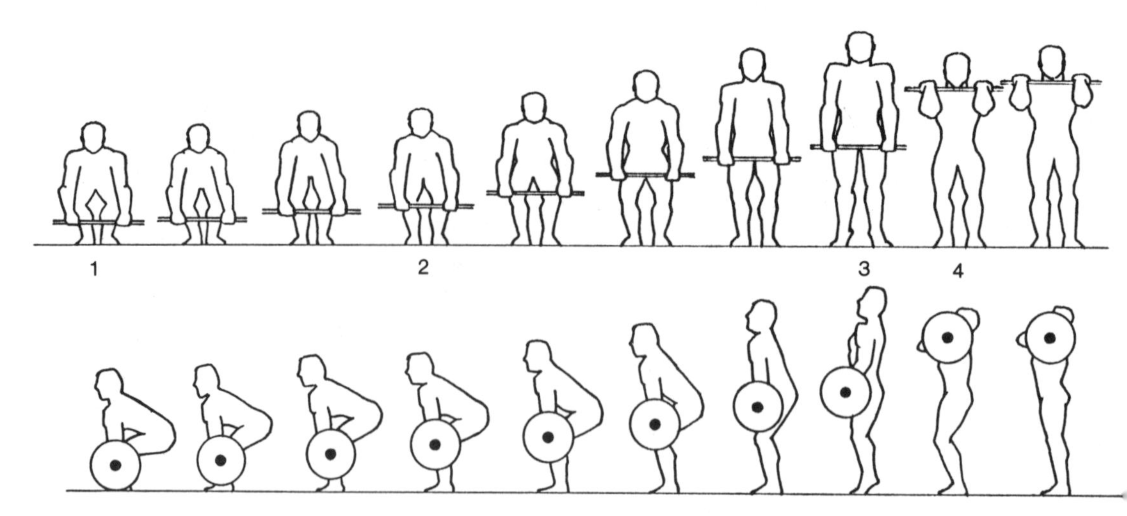

Fig. 3.2 The power clean, indicating the four key positions

slightly towards the lifter. When the bar is at knee height it is over the centre of the feet. This ensures that throughout the first stage of the lift the athlete remains in balance.

Another way to create a mental picture of this shift from KP 1 to KP 2 is to imagine separate strings attached to the shoulders and posterior of the athlete with a person directly overhead elevating the strings in unison in a fashion similar to a puppeteer manipulating his puppets.

Key position 3 (KP 3)

Bar is at mid thigh height with the legs at full extension on the balls of the feet. Shoulders are shrugged, body is in an upright balanced position with the arms still straight. This position is attained by driving the hips slightly forward and upwards in an explosive manner and is a continuation of KP 2. KP 3 is sometimes referred to as the 'full extension position'.

Key position 4 (KP 4)

This is the receiving position and its characteristics are upright trunk (most important), slightly bent knees, elbows at least halfway between the vertical and horizontal, pointing forwards. Some athletes jump feet slightly sideways from the starting position while others maintain the same spacing. Either is suitable. In the transition from KP 1 to 3 considerable vertical momentum of the bar is generated. As the bar passes KP 3 the arms bend slightly outwards, i.e. the elbows pointing along the bar. At the same time the knees bend and the elbows are whipped under the bar arriving at KP 4. This last coordinated movement is the most difficult for the novice to perform correctly. From KP 4 the athlete stands erect prior to commencing the next repetition. Breath is expelled just as the finishing position is reached.

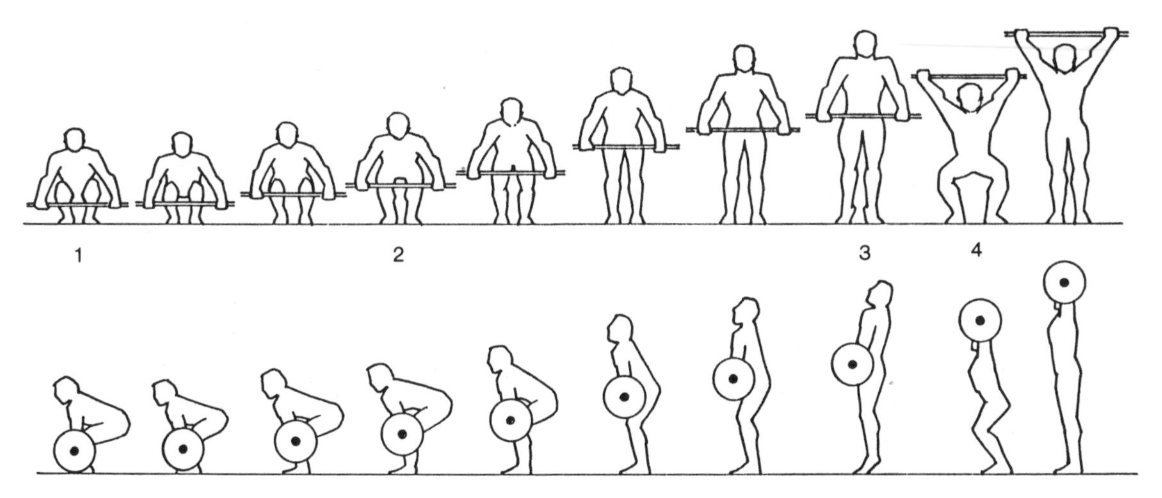

Fig. 3.3 The power snatch, indicating the four key positions

Power snatch

KP 1 to 3 are almost identical to the power clean except that a wider hand spacing is used. KP 4 differs and is slightly easier to master in comparison to the power clean. With the power snatch the momentum of the bar is continued from KP 3 by arm and shoulder forces until the bar is pulled to arm's length with the knees slightly bent at the receiving position (see KP 4). Body is upright with the bar positioned directly overhead. From KP 3 to 4 the path of the bar should be vertical and close to the body (elbows pointing along the bar is the key).

If the bar just clears the head and is then slowly pressed (pushed) to arm's length, this is an incorrect movement and indicates that the intensity (weight on the bar) should be reduced. From KP 3 to 4 the bar should travel in one continuous movement. Both the power clean and power snatch are clearly indicated in the sequence photos.

Learning procedure

In respect of the learning processes of the power clean and power snatch, the novice should spend the first two to three weeks mastering the correct technique. In some instances the movements may need to be learnt in parts i.e. KP 1 to 3 and KP 2 to 4. Only light resistance (50–60% of bodyweight) should be used in the initial period. If possible this embryonic stage should be under the guidance of an experienced coach. Some pundits tend to overemphasise the difficulty of learning these movements. They are relatively simple to perform (with adequate coaching) and it is the author's experience that athletes with reasonable skill aptitude quickly adapt to the correct pattern of execution. It is important for the novice to understand that the power clean/power snatch should be performed

Think speed of execution.

in a coordinated and continuous manner. Once technique is mastered the movements also become dynamic. Think speed of execution!

Lowering the bar

It is important to lower the bar correctly.

In order to minimise injury and maximise training effect it is important to lower the bar correctly at the conclusion of the power clean and power snatch.

Most novices have a tendency to bend the body forward at the waist (trunk flexion) and lower the bar in the form of a dynamic reverse straight leg dead lift. This places undue strain on the lower back. The best method is to slightly bend the knees (revert to KP 4) and lower the bar to mid thigh level with a minimum of forward trunk inclination. From this point slowly lower the bar to floor level, once again with a taut lower back and trunk close to vertical. This method also involves eccentric (negative) work.

Athletes of advanced level when handling limit poundages may 'unload' (drop) the bar from the finishing position, once again with a taut lower back and trunk close to vertical. This is sometimes necessary due to the extreme stress involved in lowering the bar by the previously described method. To adopt this 'unloading' method it is advisable to use rubber weightlifting discs (unless floor demolition is also desired).

Common faults

Aim for the following:

Double bodyweight back squat.

One and a half bodyweight power cleans.

The most common faults of novices (and sometimes experienced athletes) when performing the power clean and power snatch are:

• Lifting the posterior as the bar leaves the floor. This is easily recognisable by the changing angle of the back towards the horizontal (floor). This is often caused by the athlete trying to jerk the bar off the floor, rather than commencing steadily and then accelerating.

• The opposite of the above—lifting the shoulders in advance of the posterior (sometimes referred to as throwing the shoulders back early). Here again easily recognisable by the changing angle of the back towards the vertical. Remember, as was previously stated, the angle of the back remains constant in the transition from KP 1 to 2.

• Bending the arms anywhere between KP 1 to 3. This is obvious and should be discouraged. It is essential that straight arms be maintained as long as possible.

• Not attaining a completely extended or upright position as in KP 3. This, in gym jargon, is known as 'not finishing the pull' and is brought about by the exerciser being too anxious to move under the bar.

• When receiving the bar at the chest, allowing the trunk to bend backwards past the vertical (hyperflexion). This is to be avoided at all costs as stressful hyperflexion can cause lower back injury. To prevent this it is important that the athlete in the process of bending the arms

The Power Clean

The Power Snatch

Photos courtesy US Weightlifting Federation

and quickly shifting elbows under the bar, ensures that the elbows point outwards at the moment of arm bending. This prevents the bar from travelling in a small arc away from the upper body and thumping the chest with a subsequent likelihood of hyperflexion of the trunk. Assuming KP 4 with straight legs also sometimes causes undesirable hyperflexion.

In the transition of the bar from KP 2 to 4 it should be kept close to the body, i.e. almost brushing the thighs. Indeed a more advanced technique used by Olympic weightlifters involves a slight brush of the thighs with the bar as it passes the knee joint, causing the knees to slightly rebend. This action utilises both the stretch reflex mechanism and muscle elasticity surrounding the knee joint.

This particular technique is very difficult to teach and it is the opinion of many experienced coaches (and shared by the author) that this phenomenon is an anatomical accident brought about by the action of the hamstring muscle group at the knee/hip joint together with a similar action by the gastrocnemius at the knee/ankle joint.

It is the author's experience that to attempt to consciously teach this 'double knee bend' action is fraught with peril and courting disaster. What should be emphasised is that the bar be kept as close as possible to the thighs (to the point of brushing). To attempt to consciously rebend the knees causes premature weight transference, loss of balance, and unacceptable diminishment of vertical momentum of the bar. Encourage the novice to think of driving the hips forward and upwards as the bar passes the knees. This assists in bringing the knees into an appropriate position.

To conclude this chapter, listed below are some guidelines for adequate strength levels relative to

Back squat — 1½/2 times bodyweight for 1 repetition.
Power clean — 1/1½ times bodyweight for 1 repetition.
Power snatch — ¾ to 1¼ times bodyweight for 1 repetition.

While there is a wide range in these standards, i.e. 90 kg player—back squat 1R 135 kg/180 kg, this is a variable situation depending on years of training and genetics. The greater the number of training years the higher the yearly targets should be. What is important is that there be a continual upward progression, the rate of which will vary from person to person. Here body types play a major part. Players with considerable mesomorphic traits will make greater progress at a quicker rate *providing they make the same effort as their less gifted counterparts.*

In regard to youngsters it is difficult to generalise. Some mature physically much quicker than others and they could use the lower extremity of the guidelines as a target. For others who are slow physical maturers this would be excessive. Strength training for youngsters will be examined in a later part of this text.

4. Training Modes— Free Weights v Machines

If a man is going to be what he ought to be, he's got to be willing to put out just a little bit more.

Since the turn of the century the major form of strength training equipment has been what is now termed 'free weights'—barbells and dumbells. However in the last couple of decades a number of exercise machines have gone on the market with their designers claiming they are 'all things for all people'. In other words their product produces quicker and better results than other strength training methods.

With claims and counter claims flying thick and fast much confusing controversy was soon in evidence. Various strength training publications carried lengthy articles of heated debate by the proponents of free weights and the design staff of the machine manufacturers. In the course of the debate Newton's Laws of Motion were manipulated by both parties to the point of chaotic confusion.

These 'wonderful machines' varied greatly in design, some having hydraulic resistance, others operating on what is known as variable resistance (using either mechanical cams or variable pivots in a lever system), while some, by use of mechanical and electromagnetic devices, controlled speed of movement.

This sudden mushrooming of alternative training modes soon aroused the attention of exercise physiologists and strength coaches alike. Consequently over the past 15 years there has been a plethora of studies conducted by exercise physiologists in order to establish the superiority of one mode over the other. Acting in parallel, strength coaches were actively conducting their own 'research' in the area where it matters, the playing field!

Many of the scientific studies were conducted over a short period of time with untrained subjects.

Unfortunately the confusion continued. Many of the scientific studies were conducted over a short period of time with comparatively untrained subjects. As virtually any form of strength training produces a result under these conditions, the extrapolations were meaningless in most instances and quite often in conflict with the empirical observations of experienced strength coaches. Also certain studies were not entirely free of commercial ramifications—equipment manufacturer involvement with the likelihood of bias.

Both free weights and machines will have a positive effect on strength training.

There is no doubt that both free weights and machines will have a positive effect on strength training. However which is superior and under what circumstances is the crux of the matter. In order to evaluate the situation the different modes of training will be examined and the controversy placed in a proper perspective.

Free weights

Free weight total body movements are essential to 'power' sports.

Free weights by definition are barbells and dumbells. Using one's bodyweight as resistance is also a form of free weight training, i.e. chinning the bar, push ups and sit ups. Their advantages and disadvantages relative to machine training are outlined below.

Advantages

1. Free weight exercises can incorporate free standing total body (multiple joint/multi muscle group) movements essential in most power sports. The value of these movements has been previously discussed.

2. Because free weights are multi-planar (movement in all directions) a number of advantages arise:

(a) Many muscle groups and connective joint tissue are activated to control the path of the bar which has a positive effect on balance, coordination, muscle and connective joint tissue strength.

With free weights ultra specific exercises can be designed.

(b) Ultra specific exercises can be designed that exactly duplicate a particular movement pattern of a sport activity.

(c) Great variation of programs is possible because of the multitude of free weight exercises.

3. Free weights involve both concentric and eccentric contraction. It is generally accepted that both modes of contraction are important to strength training.

The generation of acceleration is a positive feature that separates free weights from machines.

4. When a free weight is lifted there is acceleration of the bar. This is due in part to the fact that while passing through strong leverage positions an athlete can exert a large force on the bar and it accommodates this effort by accelerating at a greater rate. This is particularly so with total body movements. This generation of acceleration is one of the major positive features that separates free weights from machines. Acceleration is a key factor in most power sports.

5. Free weights are relatively inexpensive and readily available to all, whether one lives in a large city or some distant rural area.

Disadvantages

1. It is considered in some quarters that there is a greater chance of injury with free weights. This is based on the fact that greater control is needed with free weights (see No. 2 in Advantages). However providing the exerciser employs correct technique, initially under supervision, the greater chance of injury (compared to machines) is minimal. This opinion is based on thirty years' practical experience.

2. Due to the physical laws of levers and the fact that free weights employ a constant load (i.e. the weight mass never changes) a 'sticking point' occurs in free weight movements. In other words the degree of difficulty changes at various points throughout the exercise. This means the muscle is not maximally loaded throughout the full range of motion. While this is a fact, particularly with single joint, isolation type movements, the position is far more complex concerning total body movements. These multiple joint/multi muscle group exercises feature a number of changing fulcrums together with the factor of acceleration previously mentioned. Furthermore in real life sporting situations the same laws of levers and constant mass still apply, so in terms of specificity this so called 'disadvantage' is common to most power activities such as sprinting, jumping, throwing and striking.

Machines

There are basically two types of machines, variable and accommodating resistance. There is a third group, relatively cheap and fragile, which is primarily designed for backyard consumption. While in outward appearance this type of machine resembles the variable resistance machines in use in commercial establishments, its principle of operation is very much inferior to its more expensive counterparts (and even more so when compared to the free weight mode). It could be loosely described as fragile exercise machinery that features neither variable nor accommodating resistance but still operates in a uniplanar manner.

Variable resistance machines

Machines provide a constant resistance through the full range of motion.

These machines generally incorporate some form of cam or lever system (see Fig. 4.1) in order to provide a constant resistance through the full range of motion. In a simpler sense, whether one is at the commencement, midway or finish of an exercise, it is equally as difficult to complete the movement, i.e. there is no 'sticking point'.

This is generally considered the major advantage of this type of machine, together with the fact that, like free weights, most variable resistance machines involve both concentric and eccentric contraction. Another minor advantage is that because of their uni-planar action, variable resistance machines are considered very safe to use with minimal risk of injury.

In terms of specificity to real life situations, the advantages of mechanically induced constant resistance are highly debatable, because when we run, jump, lift or throw an object, there are no cams or levers to help overcome any skeletal leverage disadvantages incurred.

Disadvantages

1. When these variable resistance machines were designed to offset the human body's natural lever disadvantages, the specifications were calculated around average body characteristics—the length of various body limbs and other variables such as muscle insertions etc. As was discussed in Chapter 2 these factors vary from one individual to another—a 65 kg 1.6 metre half back and a 100 kg back row forward or full forward are obviously structurally very different. Consequently, if one accepts the principle of variable resistance, in a lot of instances the machines only partly fulfil this role.

Machines provide a balance factor.

2. Machines provide a balance factor (movement in a single plane due to runners or guides). This limits the involvement of assistant movers, stabilisers, synergists and joint connective tissue. The main benefactors are the prime mover muscle groups. This does little for inter-muscle coordination and joint strengthening. However this feature can be an advantage in rehabilitation exercise after injury, or as an initial form of strength training for the young and the elderly.

It is impossible to perform total body movements on machines.

3. It is impossible to perform multiple joint total body movements on machines.

4. There is a considerably smaller range of exercises that can be performed on these machines compared to free weights.

5. These machines are expensive to purchase and availability is generally confined to clubs, commercial gymnasiums and more affluent schools.

The important factor of acceleration is severely limited on most machines.

6. The important factor of acceleration is severely limited because of the inherent design features. Indeed the manufacturer of one particular well known, cam type machine recommends that the exerciser uses his product in a slow, deliberate manner.

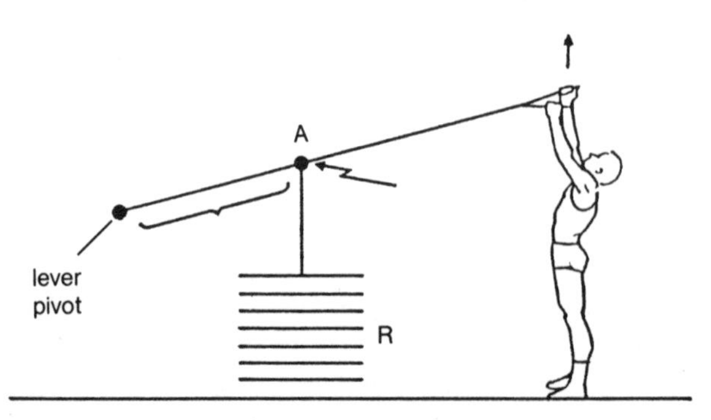

Fig. 4.1 A schematic drawing of a variable resistance machine. *Note:* Fulcrum A changes during the lifting movement, thereby varying resistance

The harder the exerciser pushes or pulls the more the machine responds.

Accommodating resistance machines

These machines are designed to 'accommodate' the efforts of the user. What this means is that the harder the exerciser pushes or pulls the more the machine responds. Conversely, the less the force applied, the less the machine responds. The resistance component on these machines varies from hydraulic to mechanical and/or electromagnetic friction.

Some of these machines also have a velocity controlling device which regulates the speed of movement (constant speed is maintained throughout the movement irrespective of effort). This velocity controlled movement is called isokinetic. The major advantage of this form of training is that there is genuine maximal loading of a muscle through the full range of motion of a particular movement, other than when operating at high velocities.

Most 'power' sports involve acceleration, a situation non specific to isokinetic principles.

Recent research would indicate that the better designed, expensive, isokinetic machines which can operate at high velocities maintain a constant speed at the high velocity setting for only a small percentage of the total range of movement. In other words, when operating at high velocities (e.g. 300° per second), there is not constant speed throughout the full range of motion because it takes the exerciser as much as until the half way point of the movement to attain this high velocity. Consequently, in the initial stage, while there is acceleration there is little resistance.

Isokinetic machines are useful in injury rehabilitation.

The more expensive isokinetic machines such as Cybex dynamometers are useful in injury rehabilitation and full range of motion muscle strength testing. Because of their constant speed factor this type of machine is a helpful training mode in sports where constant speed is a factor, such as swimming, rowing and cycling (although even these sports still involve acceleration as well as constant speed).

However, most power sports involve considerable acceleration, a situation not catered for by isokinetic principles. Another negative feature of these 'accommodating' machines is that the majority do not allow eccentric work. Indeed some of the cheaper isokinetic machines are poorly made, do not control movement speed accurately, if at all, and are little more than gimmicks.

A further negative aspect of this mode of training is that if the exerciser is lazy and does not apply maximum effort the machine responds accordingly. This can be an admirable feature when training injured limbs but is hardly the ideal situation for achieving maximal strength and power gains. Thus self motivation becomes a big factor with accommodating machines. Furthermore this type of apparatus is similar to variable resistance machines in that it is virtually impossible to perform explosive, total body movements.

Finally, as a training mode (other than rehabilitation) the better designed, more expensive isokinetic machines are not readily available to the majority of athletes. This is important because no matter how much one may desire to use this form of training, availability is the governing factor.

Summary

The majority of all the best 'power' athletes train predominantly on free weights.

Overall it is the author's opinion (and one that is shared by the majority of competent strength coaches) that for maximising the development of strength and power, particularly in sports where these commodities play a major part, free weights are the superior mode. One of the major factors influencing this statement is the benefits to be derived from total body movements, both in respect to acceleration and the excellent neuromuscular transfer to the intra and inter muscle coordination required in explosive complex athletic movements.

Empirically, the majority of the best 'power' athletes in the world train predominantly on free weights to maximise strength development. Athletes are extremely pragmatic and will generally gravitate to the mode that produces the best result.

All the best field athletes (hammer throwers, shot putters, discus) base their strength training on total body movements such as the squat, power clean, jerk and power snatch. Throwing events in althetics, together with Olympic weightlifting, epitomise the concept of power in sport. Both these activities involve high levels of strength coupled with great speed of movement. Eastern bloc athletes in all disciplines use free weights as the basis of their strength training programs. For almost two decades the multiple joint, total body movements have featured prominently in strength programs for American football. Indeed American football players are noted for their size, strength, speed and mobility.

On the local scene, Martin Vinnicombe, Australia's world champion sprint cyclist, is a free weight exponent of some considerable ability, having squatted in excess of 200 kg! The national rowing eight, domiciled at the Australian Institute of Sport, bases its strength training on free weights with squats and power cleans as the core movements. The fact that the national rowing eight won the world championship in 1986 is a reflection on the value of free weights.

Free weights have many advocates in all three football codes. Kelvin Giles, former Olympic Games athletic coach for Great Britain and former head athletic coach at the Australian Institute of Sport, has been the strength and fitness trainer with the Canberra Raiders rugby league team since 1987 and is heavily oriented towards free weights. Perhaps it is no coincidence that after many years in the competition 'wilderness' the Raiders made their first Sydney rugby league grand final in 1987 and subsequently emerged premiers in 1989. Indeed there have been many former (and current) players and coaches, such as Jack Gibson, John Peard, Laurie Frier, Wayne Pearce and Warren Ryan, to name a few, who are free weight enthusiasts. Ryan, apart from his success in rugby league, was a weightlifter of some note and represented Australia in the shot putt at the Commonwealth Games.

The same can be said of rugby union, while in Australian Rules star players such as Kelvin Templeton, Simon Beazley, Brian Wilson, Jim Edmonds, Bill Barrett and Barry Cable are part of the free weight brigade.

Over a thirty year involvement (both as a coach and participant) in strength training the author has witnessed numerous free weight exponents experimentally convert to machine modes for various time spans. Without exception their free weight performance has deteriorated. However accomplished free weight athletes can perform equally as efficiently on machines with very little exposure to that mode of training. In other words, *free weight strength is more 'convertible'.*

Free weight strength is more 'convertible'.

Bill Starr, in his excellent text published in 1977, *The Strong Shall Survive* (strength training for American football), emphasises this 'convertibility' and the overall superiority of free weights. Dr John Garhammer of the Department of Kinesiology, UCLA, California and Dr Mike Stone of the National Strength Research Centre, Alabama, USA have published numerous articles in the National Strength and Conditioning Association Journal proclaiming the superiority of free weights. Dr Pat O'Shea, a professor at Oregon State University, in his book *Scientific Principles and Methods of Strength Fitness* cautions against the overuse of 'guided apparatus' since it hinders development of neuromuscular coordination as well as antagonistic and assistant muscles. At the 1987 Elite Coaches Seminar held at the Australian Institute of Sport and organised by the Australian Coaching Council, Professor Dietmar Schmidtbleicher, a world renowned authority on strength training, spoke on the superiority of free weight training and the fact that it had the greatest carry over to athletic ability.

This litany of testimony could proceed *ad infinitum*. However, to place the overall situation in a proper perspective, what has been said regarding free weights does not mean there is not a place for machines in strength training.

In sports where strength and power are not major factors, the difference between modes would narrow.

In sports where strength and power are not major factors the difference between the modes would narrow. For the very young and older person, machines, because of their single plane operation and lesser joint stress, may be the preferable mode of training. There is no doubt machines can play a big part in rehabilitation by virtue of muscle isolation and accommodation of effort, acting as a precursor for the rehabilitee to resume more intense free exercise.

For maximal strength and power free weights are superior.

For the commercial gym operator who seeks to provide some form of basic 'muscle fitness' for the average 'get fit' enthusiast, the machines can be very useful. They require less supervision than free weights, exercise technique is simple and they are aesthetically pleasing—three good reasons for commercial utilisation. Less supervision, simple techniques and lesser joint stress can also make machines an attractive proposition for schools.

However, to reiterate the opening paragraph of this summary—*For maximising strength and power, multiple joint/multi muscle group free weight training should occupy the major part of a strength training program.*

Where to train

For the football player the number one choice would be a fully equipped gymnasium that features Olympic style free weight bars and rubber discs, exercise weights and dumbells together with some machines—the reader will see in the chapter on programming that some machine exercises are included.

However, if for financial or geographical reasons this is impossible, then the next choice would be to purchase a set of free weights (including dumbells), squat racks and a bench and train at home in the garage etc., preferably with some fellow players. Training at home alone for any length of time requires considerable self motivation. Also having training partners adheres more closely to safety principles for free weight training.

Bottom of the list for training venues would be the upmarket commercial establishments that cater predominantly for the business person, and whose major (and quite often only) mode of strength training is machines.

5. Warm Up and Stretching

The very best kind of pride is that which compels a man to do his very best even if no one is watching.

Warm up and stretching improves physical performance and prevents injury.

In this modern era the vast majority of football players and coaches are familiar with the ritual of warming up and stretching. Whether at the training ground or match venue, players at all levels of football participate in some form of warm up, generally a slow jog or callisthenics, and then perform a series of stretching movements. This preparatory workout is performed with a view to improving physical performance and preventing injury. For strength training, warm up and stretching are as important as with other football related activities.

Physiological aspects of warm up and stretching

A thorough stretching routine, preceded by a warm up which increases blood and muscle temperature, should improve athletic performance through the following mechanisms:

(a) Increased rate and strength of muscle contraction.

(b) Increased muscle coordination through related movements.

(c) Improved cardiovascular and respiratory efficiency, i.e. the adaptation of the heart to exercise stress is improved and likewise oxygen delivery to working muscles also benefits.

(d) Lessening of the possibility of injury through increased muscle elasticity and improved joint range of motion. This aspect is also important for skill efficiency in football. For example flexibility is important in sprinting.

Since temperature affects the extensibility of the body components involved in flexibility, it is particularly important to remember that stretching routines should be performed after a suitable warm up in order to achieve the best results and reduce the potential risk of stretching induced injuries.

Practical aspects of warm up and stretching

Stationary cycling is an excellent method of increasing body temperature.

General warm up In terms of strength training one of the best methods of increasing body temperature is the stationary exercise cycle. This type of activity is also beneficial to the knee area and the most suitable way of preparing this joint for the stresses of squatting, power cleans and the like. In the absence of a stationary cycle, skipping or continuous callisthenics for five minutes are acceptable alternatives.

Specific warm up This relates to warm up activities specific to the skill. For instance after general warm up and stretching, sprinters would indulge in a number of half and three quarter pace run throughs. Specific warm up for strength training simply involves commencing an exercise at a low level of intensity, i.e. 40/50% of 1RM, and proceeding with moderate increments until the designated intensity for a particular exercise is reached. This is more fully detailed in Chapter 7, 'Programming'.

Stretching

There are three recognised methods of stretching, classified as ballistic, static and PNF.

Ballistic stretching can cause minute scarring of muscle tissue.

Ballistic stretching aims to achieve increased range of motion around a joint by repetitive bouncing motions. This form of stretching, while considered effective, has been virtually abandoned by most exercise authorities because the series of pulls or jerks on the resistant muscle tissue can cause minute scarring of the tissue.

Static stretching, an effective and popular technique, involves passively stretching a given muscle by placing it in a maximal position of stretch and holding it there for an extended period of time. Recommendations for the optimal time for holding this stretched position range from ten to sixty seconds. A good compromise would be twenty to thirty seconds, repeating the stretch of each muscle group three to four times. The term 'maximal position of stretch' means stretch to the point of moderate discomfort.

PNF (Proprioceptive Neuromuscular Facilitation) is a form of stretching that combines static stretching and muscle contraction. One disadvantage of some forms of this technique is that they require a partner.

There are a number of different PNF techniques for stretching, including slow-reversal-hold, contract-relax and hold-relax methods. The simplest of these, and equally as effective, is the hold-relax method. If one uses a common hamstring stretching technique as an example the procedure would be as follows:

While you lie on your back with the knee extended and the ankle flexed at 90°, a partner passively flexes your leg at the hip joint to the point where moderate discomfort is felt. At this point you begin pushing against your partner resistance by contracting the hamstring muscle group. The

Fig. 5.1 Stretching exercises using the technique of proprioceptive neuromuscular facilitation

Fig. 5.2 Static stretches

resistance by your partner is such that there is no reverse movement, i.e. it is an isometric contraction. This contraction should never be explosive but involve a gradual increase in effort for the first two seconds which is then sustained for an additional four seconds. At the conclusion of the isometric contraction the hamstrings are relaxed and the range of motion is increased by contracting the opposite muscle group, in this case the hip flexors, in other words raising the leg through a greater angle. This manoeuvre should be unaided or, at the most, assisted by only light pressure from a training partner. This procedure is repeated several times.

A major advantage of this type of PNF stretching is that a number of basic stretches can be performed without a partner. For instance in the hamstring stretch described above, a towel or length of rope looped under the foot would serve the same purpose as a partner, i.e. one can push against the towel to achieve the isometric contraction. When increasing the range of motion after the isometric contraction do not pull the leg with the towel. Allow the hip flexors to move the leg.

In summary, for solo strength training a combination of static and hold-relax PNF stretching is the preferred option.

6. The Exercises

The reason most men do not achieve more is because they do not attempt more.

The components of the various programs for developing strength and power are its individual exercises. This chapter is all about how to correctly perform those movements most suitable for building strength, power and muscle hypertrophy in football players. There are many more exercises than those listed in this text. Indeed bodybuilding publications document some hundred odd movements.

The value of total body movements has previously been highlighted.

However many are similar to each other with minor modifications. Also quite a large number are single joint sectional movements involving single muscle groups. While these types of exercises are fine for the sport of bodybuilding and, in some instances, rehabilitation after injury, the value of multiple joint/multi muscle group free weight exercises has previously been extolled.

This does not mean that there are no machine or single joint isolation type exercises in the training programs. Indeed a number of these exercises are utilised, but in the majority of instances they play a secondary role to core movements. In defence of sectional movements, both neck and mid torso (stomach/lower back) movements would be classified in this category, and these body parts should receive high priority in all football programs.

The reader may recall that in Chapter 2 mention was made of performing the concentric or 'lifting' portion of the exercise with maximum effort, i.e. elevating the weight as quickly as possible in order to maximise fast twitch muscle fibre recruitment and enhance speed strength. This applies irrespective of the intensity (resistance). Simply put, whether the athlete is using light or heavy resistance, it should be elevated at maximal speed (while maintaining movement control).

Tempo of exercise execution should be slower when training for hypertrophy.

However on the 'lowering' or eccentric part of the exercise the opposite applies, i.e. the resistance (weight) is lowered in a slow and purposeful manner. In movements involving the neck, midsection and lower back, in the interest of injury prevention, both the lowering and elevating should be carried out in a controlled steady manner. Also when training is aimed at hypertrophy, tempo of exercise execution should be slower in order to maintain tension in the muscle fibres for a longer period.

When absorbing this chapter it should be taken into consideration that only the major muscles involved (prime movers) are given for each exercise. However in the compound movements there are many other muscle groups that play a subsidiary role. Consequently there is an overlapping effect from one exercise to the next.

The core movements, power cleans, power snatches and squats, are not discussed or illustrated in this chapter. They have been thoroughly covered in Chapter 3.

Correct breathing procedure has been previously outlined. However, to reiterate, the following method should be adopted: Inhale just prior to commencing the exercise, hold the breath during exertion and exhale at or just before completion. By holding the breath during exertion the exerciser fixes the rib cage, i.e. keeps it in the same position. The rib cage is a platform on which many muscles pull and moving it is counter productive while muscles are actively exercising. Never hold breath between repetitions.

There are two basic grips involved in the listed exercises—the pronated and supinated grip. Simply put, palms on top or underneath the bar. These grips are illustrated below.

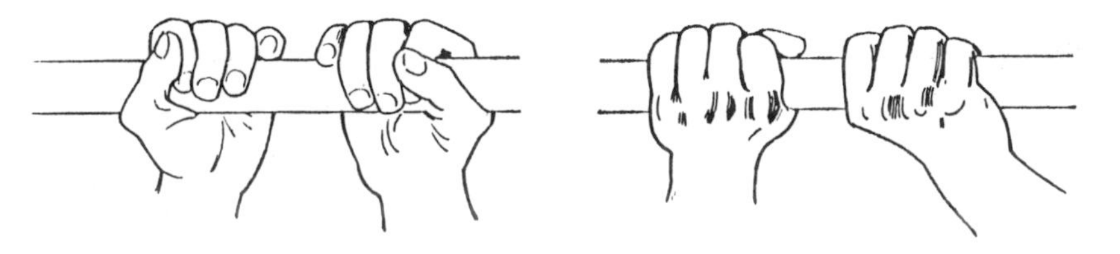

Fig. 6.1 The two basic exercise grips—pronated (right) and supinated (left)

Squat (Fig. 6.2)

Type of exercise: Core movement

Active joints are ankle, knee and hip.

Major muscles involved: Quadriceps, gluteus maximus, hamstrings. Many other muscle groups are active as stabilisers for the ankle, knee and hip joints as well as the upper vertebrae.

For complete description of execution of movement and safety features refer to Chapter 3, page 47.

Leg press (Figs 6.3, 6.4)

Type of exercise: Multiple joint/multi muscle group

Active joints are ankle, knee and hip.

Fig. 6.2 The squat

Fig. 6.3 Leg press on sled machine

Fig. 6.4 Leg press in seated position

Major muscles involved: Quadriceps, gluteus maximus, soleus, gastrocnemius.

Description of exercise: This movement is generally performed on some form of machine or apparatus with the exerciser seated or in prone position. It can also be performed on a form of sled apparatus.

Most gymnasiums have some form of seated apparatus where the exerciser grips the sides of the bench seat and extends (straightens) the legs. When the legs are in a fully extended position the calf is activated when the balls of the feet are forced forward (pointing the toes) to plantar flex the ankle. The return to the starting position should be performed slowly in order to maximise eccentric contraction. The leg press and variations suffer from the 'guided apparatus syndrome' and as such are inferior in comparison with the back squat.

Leg extension

Type of exercise: Single joint sectional

Active joint is knee.

Major muscles involved: Quadriceps.

Description of exercise: This movement is best performed on a machine. While it can be duplicated using an 'iron boot', this is not as effective in comparison with most modern machines. It is performed from a seated position with knees just over the edge of the bench. The legs are extended until they are straight, then returned slowly (resisting the weight) to starting position.

As an overall power movement this exercise rates poorly.

This movement isolates the quadriceps and is sometimes used for knee rehabilitation following injury. However in some types of knee injury leg extensions can have an adverse effect and qualified medical advice should be sought. As an overall power movement and leg strengthener this exercise rates poorly.

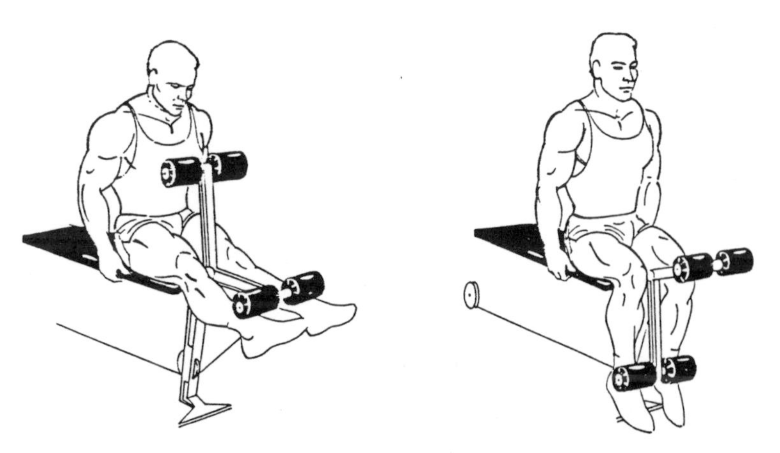

Fig. 6.5 Thigh extension on leg extension machine

Leg curl

Type of exercise: Single joint sectional

Active joint is knee.

Major muscles involved: Hamstrings.

Description of exercise: Here again this is a movement that can be performed with either a weighted 'iron boot' or on numerous machines. In all instances the exercise simply involves flexing the leg until it is in a fully bent position. In reality leg curls are the opposite of leg extensions and some machines perform both tasks.

The hamstring muscles are very active in the performance of total body movements.

The hamstring group is also very active in the performance of total body movements, particularly power cleans and snatches, and plays a major part in sprinting and jumping. In some instances a footballer may need to selectively strengthen the hamstrings because of an inherent weakness and this is where the major value of leg curls lies. Hamstring strength is extremely important in sprinting.

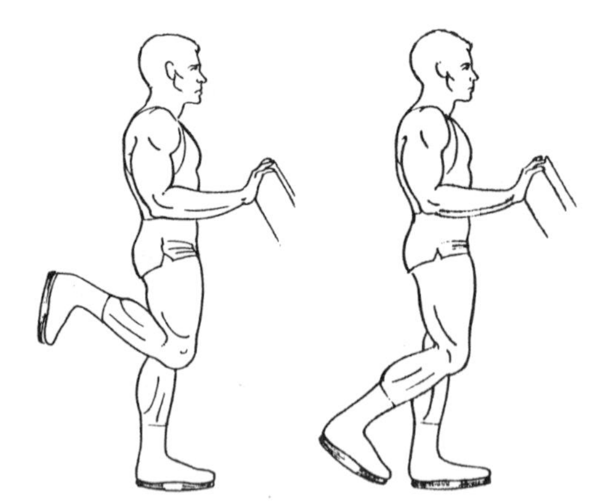

Fig. 6.6 Leg curl performed with weighted boots

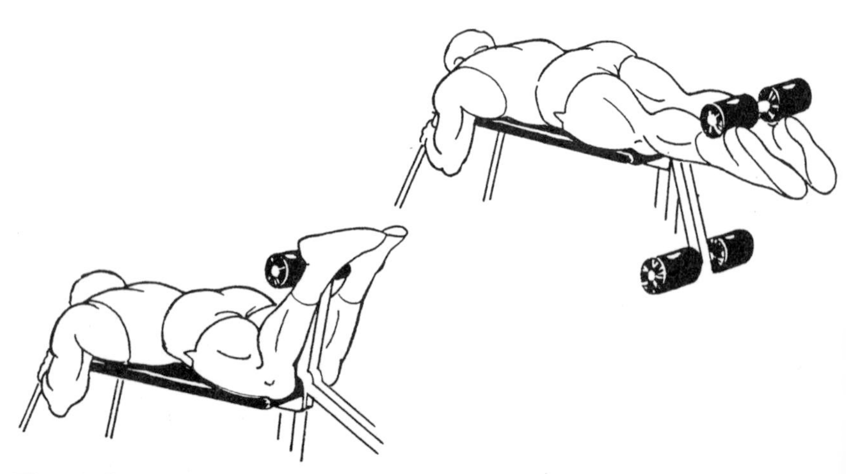

Fig. 6.7 One at a time thigh biceps curl on leg extension machine

Calf raises

Type of exercise: Single joint, sectional

Active joint is ankle.

Major muscles involved: Soleus, gastrocnemius.

Description of exercise: There are a number of variations of this exercise. It can be performed with a dumbell, barbell, on various machines and with a training partner perched on the exerciser's lower back ('donkey calf raises').

The movement simply involves rising on one's toes. To increase the range of movement (and effectiveness) at the ankle joint, most variations of the exercise can be performed with the balls of the feet supported on a board several centimetres thick.

Stair, hill and sand running, together with cycling, also strengthens the calves.

Calf strength is important in sprinting and jumping. However it should be remembered that leg presses, power cleans and speed strength activities such as stair/hill/sand running, cycling and plyometrics also strengthen this muscle group.

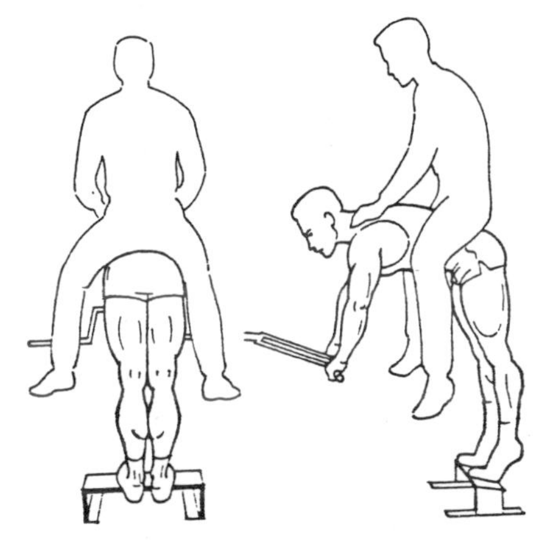

Fig. 6.8 Donkey toe raise (main calf muscles)

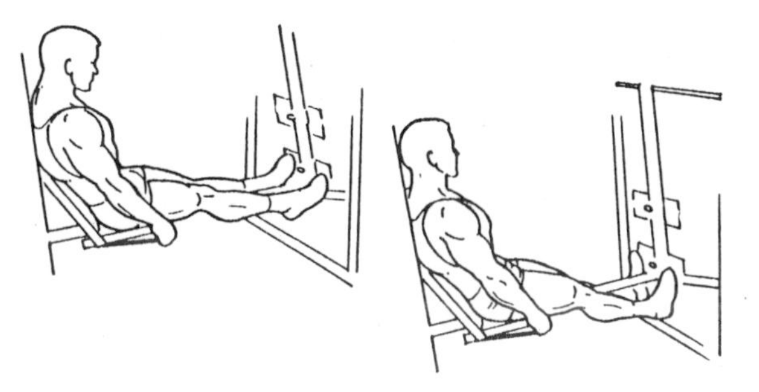

Fig. 6.9 Seated lower pad toe raise on universal type leg press machine (main calf muscles)

Fig. 6.10 Barbell toe raise (main calf muscles)

Fig. 6.11 Standing dumbell one legged toe raise (main calf muscles)

Bench step ups

Type of exercise: Multiple joint/multi muscle group

Active joints are ankle, knee and hip.

Major muscles involved: Quadriceps, gluteus maximus, erector spinae, hip flexors and extensors.

Description of exercise: This movement is performed on a bench approximately 45–55 cm high depending on the height of the exerciser. The height of the bench should be such that knee joint angle is approximately 90° when the foot is resting on top of the bench. The resistance can be either dumbells or a barbell across the shoulders. Dumbells are the preferable option if the exercise is performed as a speed strength movement. Heavier weights can be accommodated as a barbell supported across the shoulders but the exercise then becomes slow and cumbersome.

Once the exerciser becomes accustomed to the technique of the movement, dumbells of substantial proportions are well within the scope of adult football players. Indeed the combination of back squats (double leg movement) with step ups (single leg) is ideal for developing strength and power specific to sprinting. Also step ups performed with moderate resistance and relatively high repetitions are an excellent total body cardiorespiratory exercise for inclusion as a circuit station.

When performing step ups the exerciser should aim at developing rhythm and speed.

Execution of the movement is simple. Firstly the right foot is placed on top of the bench prior to stepping upon it with both feet, the body at full extension. Immediately the left leg is lowered to the ground and back onto the bench, the body once again at full extension. This pattern is continued, i.e. left leg up, left leg down, right leg up, right leg down in a rhythmical motion. The stepping leg should do all the work on the

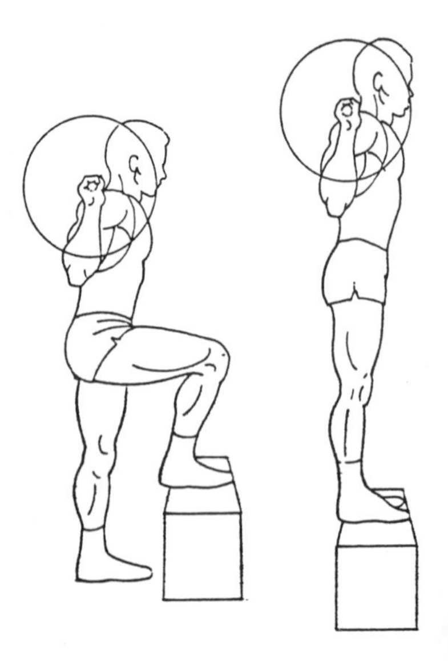

Fig. 6.12 Bench step up

way up with no assistance from the trailing leg (i.e. no pushing off the ground). Another important factor is that the change of feet takes place quickly on top of the bench when the body is at full extension. There can be a tendency to cross the feet over in mid air, which restricts full body extension and consequently reduces range of motion. This method of performing step ups has far more 'athletic' specificity than the more conventional method where from the position on top of the bench at full body extension the left leg is lowered followed by right, then left leg up followed by right.

When performing step ups the exerciser should aim at developing rhythm and speed, particularly when using only bodyweight or light resistance. This exercise, squats and squat jumps all play a big part in speed strength.

Bench press and its variations

Type of exercise: Multiple joint, multi muscle group

Active joints are elbows, shoulder and shoulder girdle.

Major muscles involved: Deltoids, triceps and pectoralis major.

Exercise description: The bench press is an extremely well known and popular exercise used extensively by all sportspersons irrespective of their activity. In some circles it is regarded as the ultimate upper body exercise and is often linked with the squat and power clean under the collective heading of 'the big three'.

It certainly doesn't deserve the 'star status' of squatting and power cleans.

However while bench pressing and its variations are a valuable compound exercise, it certainly doesn't deserve the 'star status' of squatting and power cleans. Indeed exercises of a similar nature performed in a standing position (e.g. all forms of overhead pressing/push pressing) are equally as important and far more specific to most sports.

The exercise can be performed with either a barbell or dumbells. When using the bar, the exerciser assumes a supine position on a flat or incline bench and either has the bar assisted to him by a training partner or removes the bar from a set of uprights attached to the end of the bench. A pronated or 'palms under' grip is used with hand spacing about a hand span wider than shoulder width.

To commence the movement the bar is slowly lowered until it lightly touches the chest. It is then pressed to arm's length. When performing the exercise avoid the following: (a) lowering the bar quickly and bouncing off it, (b) raising the posterior off the bench and bridging the mid upper back area, (c) any form of lateral twisting of the trunk to assist in elevating the bar.

Finally, remember the correct breathing sequence—inhale either just before or as you start lowering the bar, exhaling just prior to or at the completion of the movement.

Fig. 6.13 Medium grip barbell bench press

Fig. 6.14 Close grip barbell bench press

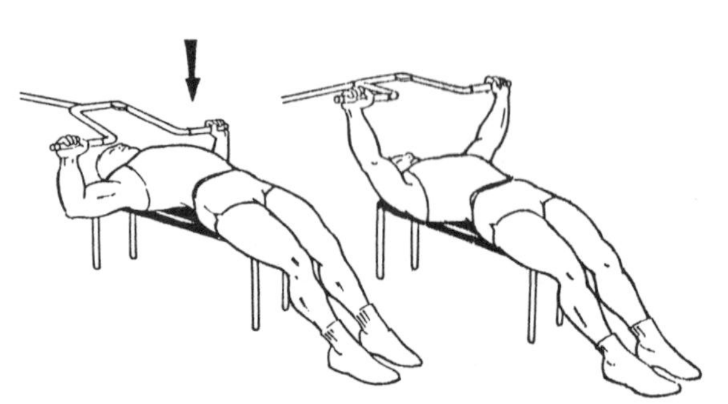

Fig. 6.15 Bench press on universal machine

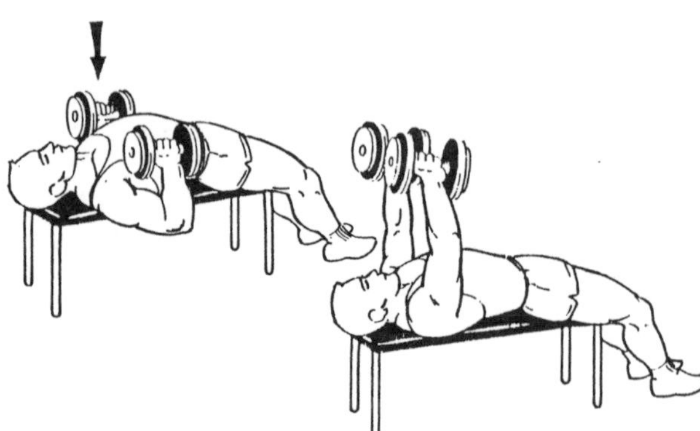

Fig. 6.16 Flat dumbell prone

Fig. 6.17 Medium grip incline barbell bench press

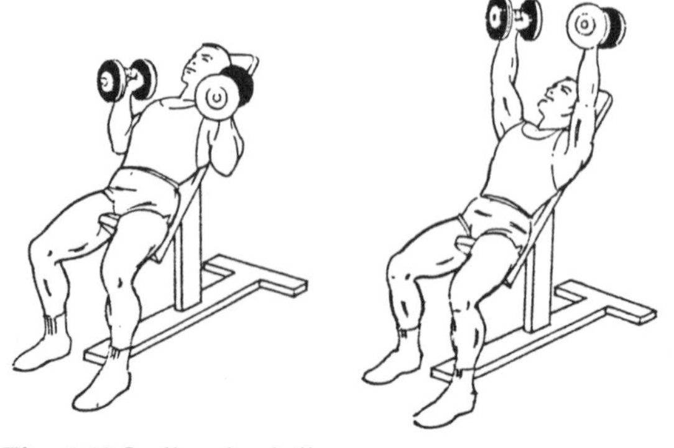

Fig. 6.18 Incline dumbell prone

There are a number of variations to this exercise. It can be performed on an incline bench where it has a greater effect on the upper part of the chest and the frontal deltoids. It can also be performed with dumbells. In some instances, particularly when using heavy dumbells, it is necessary to have the dumbells handed to the exerciser by training partners. Dumbells require considerably more control than the bar, as there are greater multi directional forces involved.

Bench pressing can also be performed with a shoulder width (or less) grip, resulting in considerably more stress on the triceps muscles (the connecting link). This results in a reduction in the amount of weight that can be elevated. There are a number of bench pressing machines that are popular in most gymnasiums. However because of the mechanical guided path of resistance (and in some cases speed control) the machines are not as effective as the free weight movements.

When handling near limit poundages always have a 'spotter' on standby.

In terms of safety, when handling near limit poundages in bench pressing always have a 'spotter' on stand by to prevent injury through loss of control or being caught with the bar across the chest and unable to move it.

Parallel bar dips

Type of exercise: Multiple joint, multi muscle group

Active joints are elbows, shoulder and shoulder girdle.

Major muscles involved: Deltoids, triceps and pectoralis major.

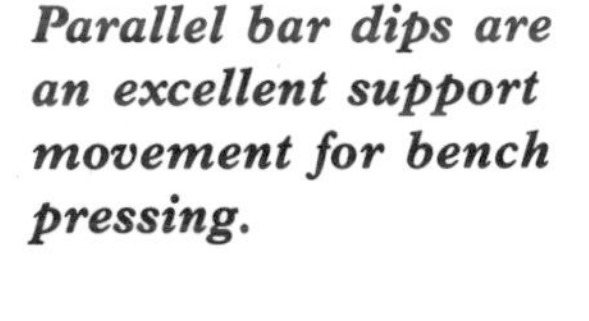

Parallel bar dips are an excellent support movement for bench pressing.

Description of exercise: This movement is performed by placing the body at arm's length between a set of parallel bars and then lowering as far as possible before pressing back into the starting position. Avoid body swing.

After a period of time the exerciser will be able to perform this movement for many repetitions. At this stage resistance should be incorporated by attaching weight plates to a waist belt. Parallel bar dips are an excellent support movement for bench pressing.

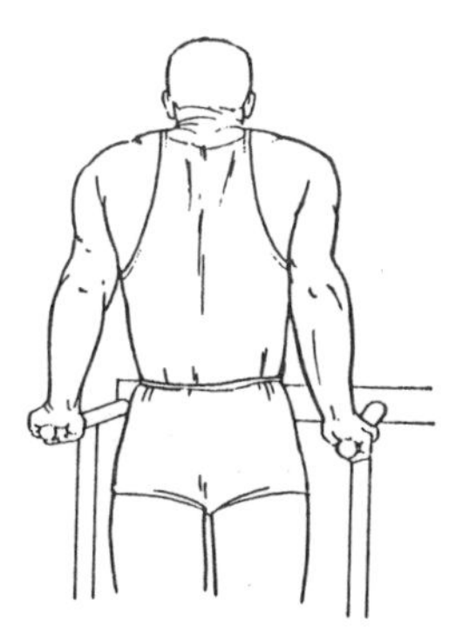

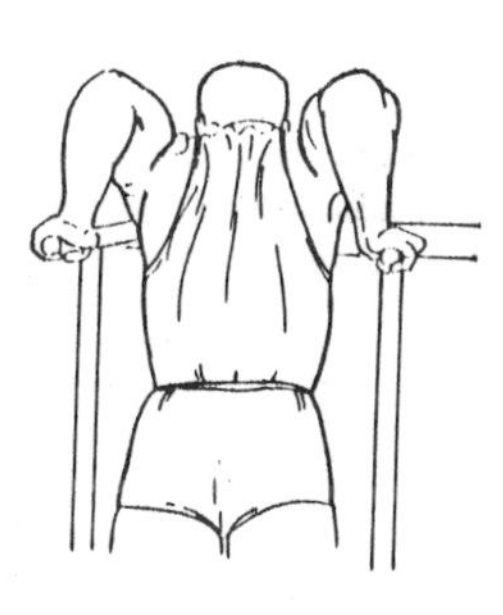

Fig. 6.19 Dips (pectorals and triceps)

Overhead pressing and variations

Type of exercise: Multiple joint, multi muscle group

Active joints are elbows, shoulder and shoulder girdle.

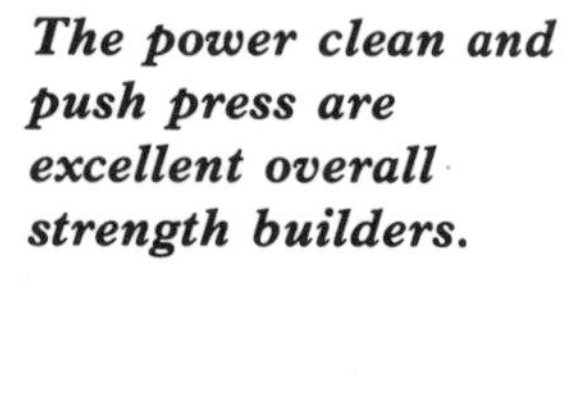

The power clean and push press are excellent overall strength builders.

Description of exercise: There are a number of variations of overhead pressing. This movement may be performed with a bar from either the frontal position with a bar supported across the clavicles and deltoids or in the 'behind the neck' position with the bar resting across the upper back. It can also be executed with dumbells. This is an extremely effective variation because, as with the bench press, it requires greater control with dumbells. Indeed the power cleaning and elevating of dumbells overhead in a standing position is a *numero uno* movement in the same category as power movements such as the squat and power cleans with the bar. All of the abovementioned variations can also be performed seated on a bench. The seated position increases the degree of difficulty.

Execution of these movements is simple. Whether bar or dumbells, the implement is cleaned from the floor as in power cleans and after a short pause at the chest to adjust breathing, is pressed overhead to arm's length. From this position it is slowly lowered to the shoulders and the movement is repeated for the required number of repetitions. The stomach and lower back should be kept taut (static contraction) and leaning back should be avoided during the movement. Knees remain locked during the standing variations.

Fig. 6.20 Seated barbell press in front and behind neck (front and outer deltoids)

Fig. 6.21 Standing military press (front and outer deltoids)

As with the bench press, overhead pressing machines are available in most gymnasiums. They are generally used in a seated position and possess the same disadvantages as bench pressing machines.

With the front press grip space is about shoulder width. The behind the neck version is best done with a slightly wider grip. Pronated grip (palms on top of the bar) is used in cleaning the bar, bearing in mind that when it is at shoulder level the palms are then under the bar. With dumbells the movement can be performed the same as with the bar or with the handles at 90° to the bar. The dumbells can be pressed together or alternatively, with the former being superior.

An excellent overall strength builder is the push press with the bar. In this variation, the bar is power cleaned to the shoulders as previously described for the overhead press. However to commence the movement of the bar the exerciser uses a short forceful dip of the knees (a plyometric action). As the bar passes eye level the knees lock and the arms vigorously propel the bar to the fully locked position overhead. Once again the bar is slowly lowered to starting position.

Fig. 6.22 Standing palms in dumbell press (front and outer deltoids)

Fig. 6.23 Standing barbell press behind neck (front and outer deltoids)

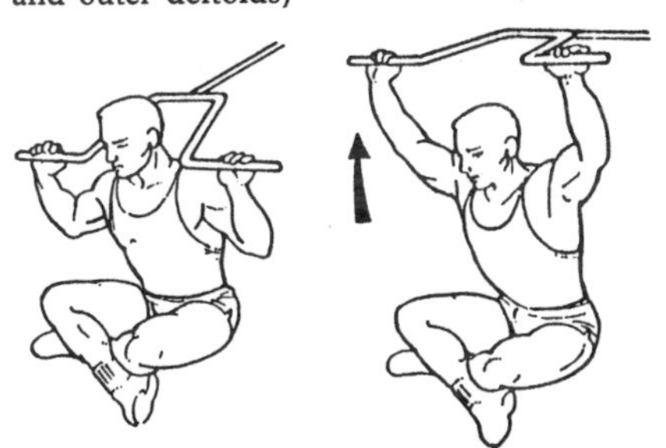

Fig. 6.24 Seated facing out press on universal machine (front and outer deltoids)

Fig. 6.25 Seated palms out alternated dumbell press (front and outer deltoids)

Upright rowing

Type of exercise: Multiple joint, multi muscle group

Active joints are elbow, shoulder and shoulder girdle.

Major muscles involved: Deltoids, trapezius and arm flexors.

The barbell version is superior.

Description of exercise: This is another excellent shoulder movement. It is generally performed with a barbell and is executed by holding the bar across the thighs with a fully extended arm position, pronated narrow grip, and then raising the bar upwards close to the body by bending the elbows until it reaches the level of the chin, elbows at ear level. From this position it is slowly lowered to the starting position. There should be no bending of the knees prior to or during the movement, nor should there be any bending of the trunk to the front or rear. As a variation, the movement can be performed with a shoulder width grip and also with dumbells. The barbell version is superior.

Fig. 6.26 Medium grip barbell upright rowing (front deltoids and trapezius)

Chinning the bar

Type of exercise: Multiple joint, multi muscle group

Active joints are elbow, shoulder, shoulder girdle.

Major muscles involved: Latissimus dorsi, pectoralis major and minor, rhomboids, elbow flexors.

Chins generally favour the lighter person.

Description of exercise: Chinning the bar is a traditional movement practised or attempted by everyone at some stage of his life. It is an excellent compound upper body exercise with one major drawback—not everyone can execute the movement. It is an exercise that generally favours the lighter, stronger athlete. Heavier people, unless exceptionally strong,

Fig. 6.27 Close grip front chin (lower lats)

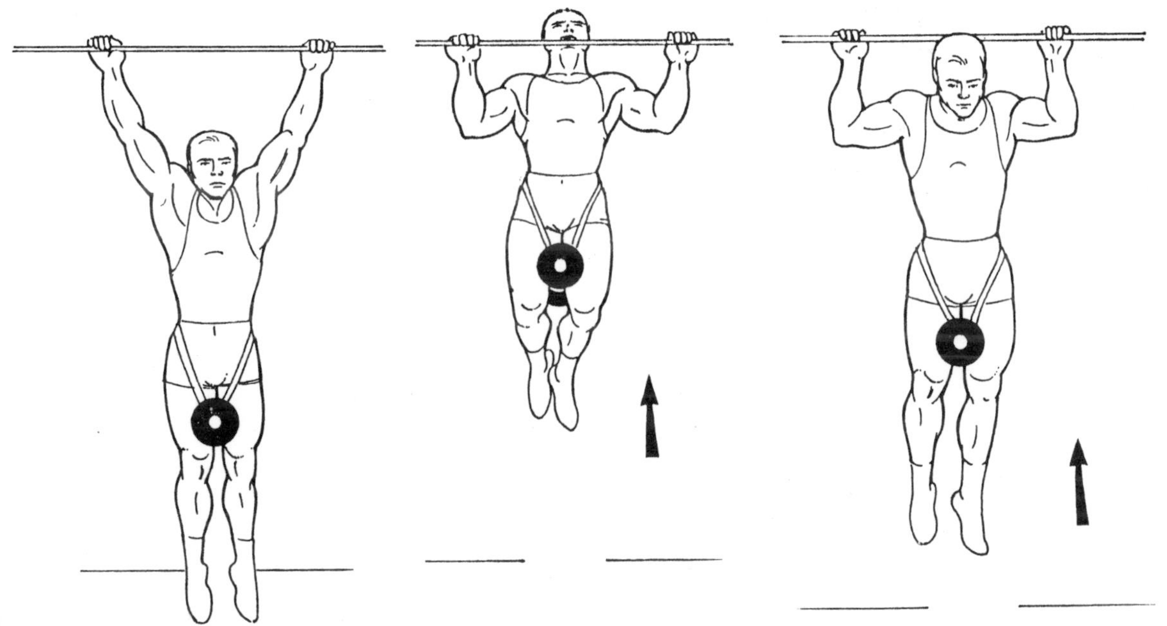

Fig. 6.28 Wide grip weighted front to rear chin (lats)

struggle to perform many repetitions. The major cause of this is that minimum resistance is total bodyweight. In the majority of exercises one can reduce the resistance if it is difficult. However short of amputating a leg this is impossible with chins. The only way this bodyweight can be lessened is to have a training partner give you a lift. This is unsatisfactory and generally not recommended.

Fig. 6.29 Wide grip front lat pulldown (upper lats)

Fig. 6.30 Wide grip rear lat pulldown (upper lats)

For those exercisers who are strong enough to perform this movement there are a number of variations based around different grips and their width. Both pronated and supinated grips, narrow and wide spacing, together with behind the neck and in front of the chin are the major variations. Basically the same muscle groups are involved in all movements. However the degree of involvement varies with the position. For instance wide frontal chins with a pronated grip accentuate the upper chest, whereas the same movement behind the neck favours the upper back. Narrowing the grip places more stress on the elbow flexors.

Performance of the movement is simple—the exerciser assumes a hanging position on the chin bar, arms fully extended with the appropriate grip and hand spacing. From this position the body is elevated until either chin or lower rear portion of the neck touches the bar. After slowly lowering to the starting position the movement is repeated.

Resistance can be increased by hanging weights around the waist. Different variations can be performed in the one workout, i.e. one/two sets of each variation. Alternatively one variation can be performed for a number of weeks followed by another and so on.

Lat machine pull downs (Figs 6.29, 6.30)

Type of exercise: Multiple joint, multi muscle group

Active joints are elbow, shoulder and shoulder girdle.

Major muscles involved: Latissimus dorsi, pectoralis major and minor, rhomboids, elbow flexors.

Description of exercise: This movement is performed on an overhead pulley device called a 'lat machine'. This piece of equipment has been in operation in gymnasiums for many decades, long before the advent of the high tech, upmarket machines of today.

The exercise is usually performed in the seated position and involves pulling a bar (with a pronated grip) from overhead to the shoulders and then slowly returning to the starting position. The movement can be likened to chins in reverse and involves the same muscle groups. Indeed all that has been said about chinning the bar relative to grip spacings, frontal and behind the neck variations etc. applies to lat machine pull downs. The major difference is that one can use resistance less than bodyweight. This movement has wide appeal and is utilised in most programs.

The major difference is one can use resistance less than bodyweight.

Bent forward rowing and variations

Type of exercise: Multiple joint, multi muscle group

Active joints are elbow, shoulder and shoulder girdle.

Major muscles involved: Latissimus dorsi, posterior deltoids and elbow flexors.

Description of exercise: As was the case with chins and lat machine pull downs, this movement is considered to be primarily an upper back exercise. It can be performed with either a bar or dumbells and is ideal for the exerciser who cannot chin the bar and trains at home without the benefit of a lat machine.

Execution involves assuming a position with the upper torso 10° to 20° above the horizontal (see sketches below) with knees slightly bent, barbell grasped with a pronated grip slightly wider than shoulder width. From this position the bar is pulled or 'rowed' into a mid stomach position. Body movement should be minimal.

With a dumbell the exercise position is similar with the exception that one hand is placed on a bench for support. This reduces stress on the lower back. The execution with the dumbell is the same as with the barbell except that the finishing position is more to the side. After performing the required number of repetitions, the process is repeated on the alternate side. Many exercisers prefer the dumbell version because of the reduced stress to the lower back.

The dumbell version reduces stress on the lower back.

This movement can also be carried out on a floor pulley or Olympic bar as illustrated below. Muscle involvement is similar to the bar and dumbell version.

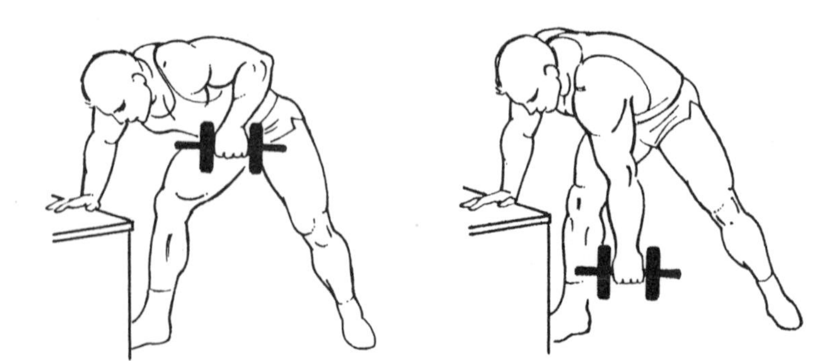

Fig. 6.31 Hand on bench one-arm dumbell rowing (upper and lower lats)

Fig. 6.32 Close grip bent over barbell rowing (lower lats)

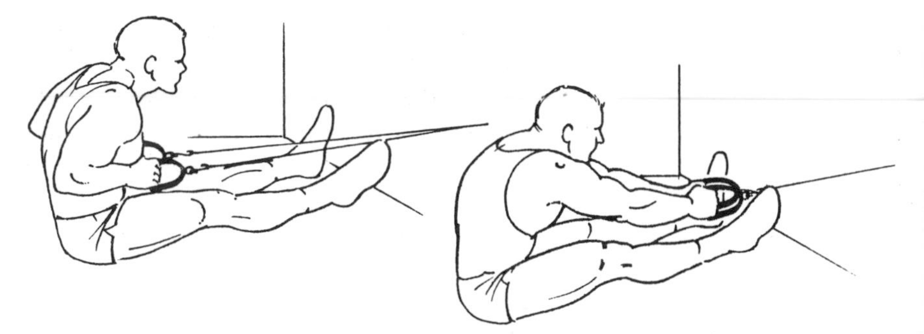

Fig. 6.33 Seated two-arm medium height lat pull in (lats)

Fig. 6.34 Standard bent over two-arm long bar rowing (lower lats)

Back raise

Type of exercise: Single joint, sectional

Active joint is intervertebral (joints in spinal column).

Major muscles involved: Spinal erectors.

Description of exercise: This movement is performed on a specially designed bench as illustrated below. It can also be carried out on a high table or bench with some padding under the hips and the ankles held by a training partner.

To execute the movement the exerciser assumes a face down position lying horizontally on the bench or table with spine fully flexed and head near the floor. The edge of the bench/table should be just below waist level. This is important as too much upper body projection stresses the hamstring group, whereas the purpose of the exercise is to isolate the spinal erectors. From the fully flexed spinal position (i.e. head near floor) the lower back should be rounded. As the upper body is raised towards finish position the lower back is flattened.

Avoid hyperextension of the trunk.

Avoid hyperextension of the trunk, i.e. arching up past parallel, as it places excessive stress on lower vertebral discs. As the lower back is one of the weakest links in the human structure it is important to selectively strengthen this area, with back raises ideally suited to this purpose. Initially this exercise should be performed with bodyweight. However after a suitable preparatory period the average footballer should be able to perform this movement with 10 to 20 kg weight plates held behind the neck.

Fig. 6.35 Weighted hyperextension (lower back)

Fig. 6.36 Stiff legged barbell good morning (lower back)

Good mornings (Fig. 6.35)

Type of exercise: Multiple joint, multi muscle group

Active joints are hip and intervertebral.

Major muscles involved: Hamstring, gluteals and spinal erectors.

Description of exercise: This movement derives its name from the fact that there is some similarity to the 'stretch and touch your toes in the morning' syndrome that existed yesteryear (which incidentally is probably the last thing one should do in the way of stretching after rising). To perform the exercise a barbell is held firmly across the shoulder area behind the neck while the exerciser bends forward by flexion at the hips until the upper torso is almost parallel to the floor. Return slowly to the starting position.

There are a number of variations to this exercise. It can be executed with straight or slightly bent legs and with the lower back both flat and rounded. With a flat back the spinal erectors are subject to isometric (static) work, while if the back rounds on the downward movement and returns to the flat position on the upward segment, the erector spinae contract eccentrically downwards and concentrically moving back to the starting position. At the same time on downward movement the hamstrings and gluteals contract eccentrically with concentric contraction taking place when returning to the starting position.

A flat back enables the exerciser to use more resistance than in the rounded back version. Also slightly flexed knees lessen the stress on the hamstrings and consequently enable the exerciser to use more weight. In view of the fact that this movement is primarily used as a lower back exercise, the bent knee rounded back version is preferred.

In terms of rehabilitation back raises are a better choice of movement.

Overall all variations are quite stressful on the lower back and should be avoided if injury to this area is present. In terms of rehabilitation back raises are a better choice of movement.

Sit ups

Type of exercise: Single joint, sectional

Active joint is intervertebral. Depending on method of execution it can be a dual joint movement also involving the hip joint.

Major muscles involved: Abdominals and under some circumstances the hip flexors.

Much depends on the manner in which the movement is performed.

Description of exercise: The sit up is an exercise that is well known to all and sundry. Almost every person at some stage of his life has performed sit ups, even if only at school as a form of punishment for some misdemeanour. It is automatically associated with the stomach muscles (abdominals) by both sportspersons and the general public.

Unfortunately this is not totally accurate. Much depends on the manner

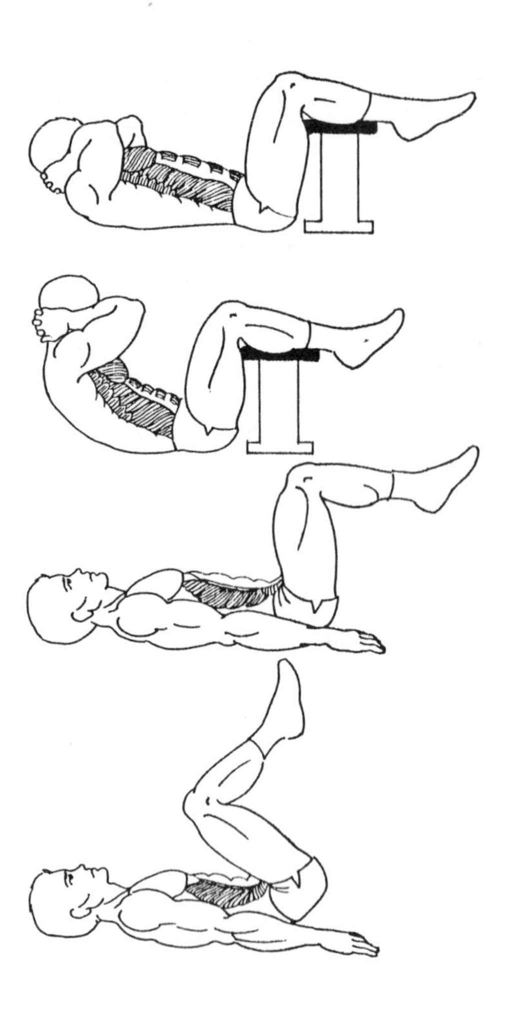

Fig. 6.37 Partial sit up or bench trunk curl (abdominals)

Fig. 6.38 Chinning bar compound leg pull in (lower abdominals and obliques)

in which the movement is performed. It is an anatomical fact that the abdominals are the principal muscle group when flexing the spine. However they play no part in hip flexion. What this means is that the sit up when performed with the legs straight is primarily exercising the hip flexor muscles with the stomach muscles playing a lesser role.

Furthermore, one of the major muscles used in hip flexion is attached to the lower lumbar region of the spine, which naturally curves inwards. Therefore excessive emphasis on this particular muscle group could in some cases aggravate or cause lower back trauma. So the purpose of sit ups should be to isolate the abdominal muscles.

The purpose of sit ups is to isolate the abdominals.

To achieve this isolation there are several options available. One is to perform the movement with bent knees. This has the effect of reducing the part played by the muscles involved in flexing the hips. However for total isolation the most effective exercise is the partial sit up, sometimes referred to as bench trunk curls. It is performed with the legs on a bench as illustrated. The range of movement of the head and shoulders is about 30–40° and the lower part of the back remains in contact with the floor. Bench trunk curls exercise the upper abdominals with little effect on the lower abdominals, so some full range bent knee sit ups or bent knee leg raises on the floor/chinning bar should be included to avoid neglect of lower abdominals. What has been said concerning sit ups with straight legs applies equally to leg raises.

Reverse trunk twists

Type of exercise: Single joint, sectional

Active joint is hip.

Major muscles involved: Internal and external obliques.

Description of exercise: This movement is performed lying on the back on the floor with arms extended out to the sides so that they are in line

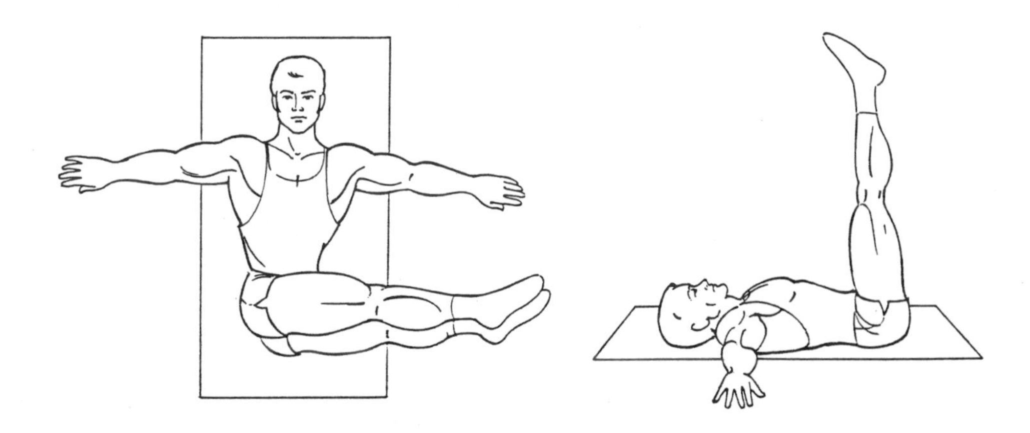

Fig. 6.39 Reverse trunk twists

with the shoulders (perpendicular to the trunk). The body and arms should form a 'T' as illustrated. Raise the legs up to a position perpendicular to the trunk. From this starting position keep feet together and lower them to the left side until the feet touch the floor. Return to the starting position and repeat the process on the right side. The cycle is then repeated until the desired number of repetitions are performed. When lowering and raising the legs be sure the shoulders maintain contact with the floor. It may be necessary to have a training partner hold the shoulders down.

As the exerciser becomes stronger in the movement, i.e. twenty to thirty repetitions each side, then resistance can be increased by using wrap around ankle weights.

Reverse trunk twists are an excellent mid section movement.

This exercise is very beneficial to all sportspersons who are involved in twisting actions, a movement often required in football. A strong mid section maximises leg and hip action, so this exercise, together with sit ups and leg raises, should receive ample attention from all football players. Reverse trunk twists involve both the abdominals and some lower back muscles and are consequently of considerable importance.

Neck exercises

Type of exercise: Single joint, sectional

Active joint is intervertebral upper spine.

Major muscles involved: Neck muscles.

Never neglect the neck.

Description of exercise: The importance of a strong neck in football has already been mentioned. This part of the human body structure is very fragile. It is also subjected to a lot of physical stress in all body contact football. Without a doubt one of the most tragic injuries a football player can sustain is intervertebral upper spine damage resulting in permanent incapacity. While a strong neck is no total guarantee against this type of injury, medical opinion is firmly of the belief that a well developed, strong neck considerably lessens the chances of serious injury in this region.

There are a number of ways to develop and strengthen the neck. The simplest and most suitable to begin with is partner assisted manual resistance movements. This involves the exerciser resisting the manipulations of his training partner (from side to side and front to back).

A more advanced movement involves the exerciser using a head strap or harness to which weights can be attacked. Assuming both a prone, supine and standing position the neck can be exercised through the same range of motion as in the partner resistance mode. Resistance can be increased by simply adding weights to the head harness.

Medical opinion is firmly of the belief that a strong neck lessens the chances of serious spinal injury.

Neck bridging exercises as used by wrestlers place extreme stress on the cervical discs and should be used with caution and only after a lengthy preparatory period on more moderate movements. Some machines have neck exercise stations which are quite effective.

Exercises such as upright rowing, power cleans and snatches, all of which involve the trapezius muscle group, also have a positive effect on neck stability.

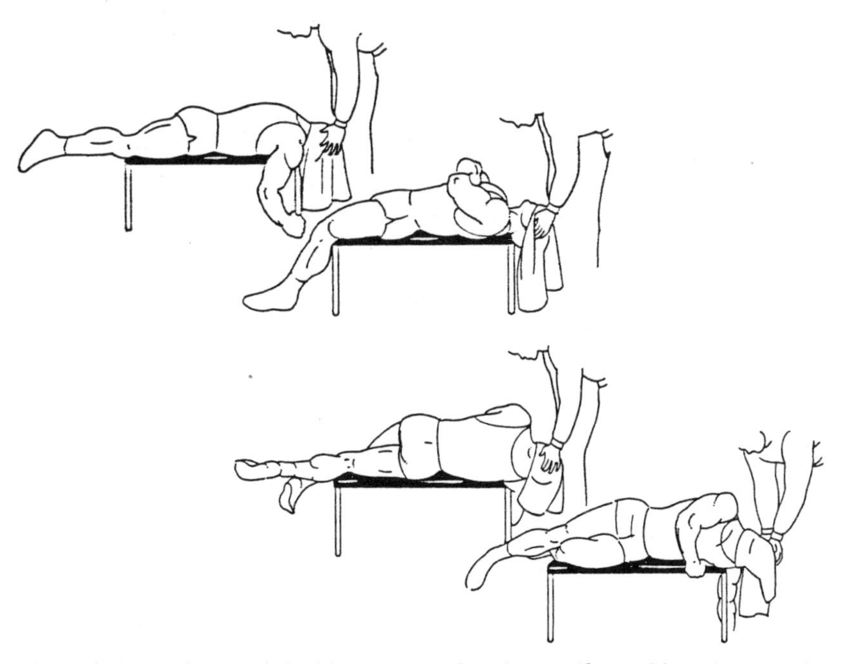

Fig. 6.40 Lying flat bench buddy system neck resistance (front, side and rear neck muscles)

Fig. 6.41 Seated buddy system neck resistance (front, side and rear neck muscles)

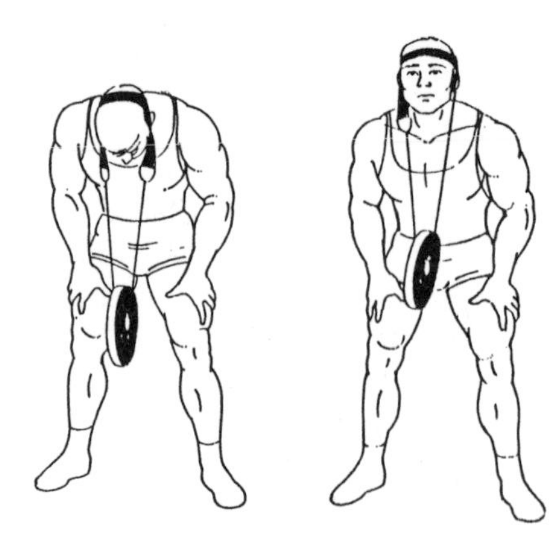

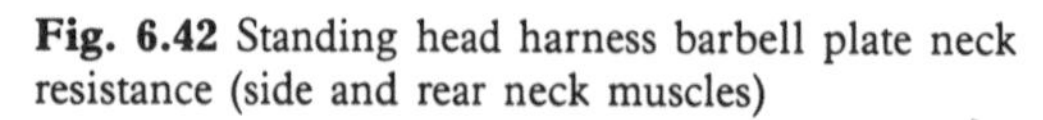

Fig. 6.42 Standing head harness barbell plate neck resistance (side and rear neck muscles)

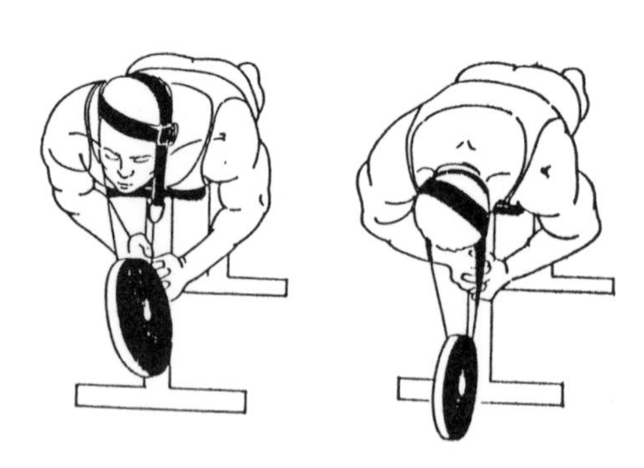

Fig. 6.43 Lying head harness barbell plate neck resistance (side and rear neck muscles)

Arm curl and variations

Type of exercise: Single joint, sectional

Active joint is elbow.

Major muscles involved: Biceps, brachialis, brachioradialis.

Description of exercise: This movement can be performed with both barbell and dumbells. It can also be performed on a pulley machine. It simply involves taking a bar or dumbells with a supinated grip while in a standing position and curling the bar (or dumbells) from the fully extended arm position to one of full flexion. Slowly return to starting position to maximise eccentric contraction. In order to isolate the arm flexor muscles there should be no movement of either the lower or upper torso.

There are a number of variations of this movement performed in a lying or seated position on various benches. They are popular with bodybuilders but have little relevance to strength training for football.

Elbow flexors are involved in many compound exercises such as power cleans, upright and forward rowing, chins, lat machine pull downs etc. Therefore if time restraints require an abbreviated program, curls would be a low priority movement.

Lat machine press downs

Type of exercise: Single joint, sectional

Major muscles involved: Triceps.

Description of exercise: This movement is performed on a lat machine and is executed by standing in front of the machine, grasping the bar with a narrow pronated grip, elbows tucked in to the sides and arms fully

Fig. 6.44 Dumbell curl (biceps)

Fig. 6.45 Barbell curl (biceps)

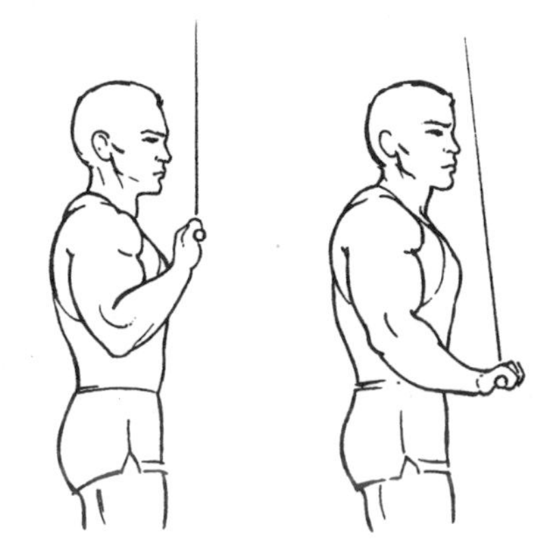

Fig. 6.46 Standing close grip triceps press down on lat machine (outer triceps)

Fig. 6.47 Standing medium grip triceps press down on lat machine (outer triceps)

flexed. From this position the bar is pressed downwards until the arms are fully extended. Elbows are maintained in the starting position throughout the movement with overall body movement minimal. From the fully extended arm position the bar is slowly resisted until it reaches starting position.

As with arm curls this movement is a low priority in abbreviated programs. All pressing movements, both overhead and on the bench, adequately exercise the triceps. Parallel bar dips are very effective in strengthening the triceps with the added advantage of chest and shoulder involvement.

Glute-ham-gastroc raise

Type of exercise: Multiple joint, multi muscle group

Active joints are knee, hip and intervertebral.

Fig. 6.48 Glute–ham–gastroc raise on specially designed bench

Major muscles involved: Gastrocnemius, gluteals, hamstring and spinal erectors.

Description of exercise: This movement is used extensively in the USSR for hamstring strength and development. It also involves the gluteus maximus, the gastrocnemius and to a lesser extent the spinal erectors. Consequently it is an exercise very relevant to the running, jumping activities of football.

However there is one major drawback. To perform the glute-ham-gastroc raise (g-h-g) correctly a special bench is needed. The design of such a bench is clearly illustrated in Fig. 6.48. The only other way to perform the g-h-g raise is to use a gymnastics pommel horse, something that is also often not readily available. Using the pommel horse (lying across the rounded surface) also requires a training partner to hold the exerciser's ankles.

To execute the movement the exerciser assumes position 1 on the apparatus. From here raise the trunk keeping the back straight. Don't bend at the waist as recommended in the back raise. The action takes place in the hip joint with the upper body and pelvic girdle acting as a unit. The trunk is raised to the point where the body is in a straight line from top to bottom as for Position 2. The action to this point has involved hip joint extension and provided tension to the upper portion of the hamstrings and gluteus maximus. There is also static contraction of the spinal erectors.

From Position 2 continue pulling up by flexing the knees until completion of the movement at Position 3. Slowly lower (eccentric work) back to the starting position. Indeed this whole movement should be performed in a slow precise manner. The second portion of the exercise (from Position 2 to 3) involves knee flexion. This creates tension in both the gastrocnemius and lower part of the hamstrings. At the same time there is continued tension on the upper portion. This action culminates in a supramaximal contraction of the hamstrings.

Once the exerciser is capable of performing about fifteen reps it would be appropriate to increase resistance by holding a light weight across the shoulders. While this movement is not included in the workout schedules listed in the chapter on programming, the experienced player (in terms of strength training years) could substitute the g-h-g raise for leg curls. The obvious proviso would be equipment availability.

7. Programming

Fatigue makes cowards of us all.

What is programming?

Programming is the compilation of a group of exercises to a set plan in order to achieve a maximal result in the most efficient manner possible. The major factors are volume and intensity of load, frequency of training, type of exercise, variability and specificity.

The need to plan

Fail to plan is plan to fail.

There is an adage that says 'Fail to plan is plan to fail'. Perhaps in respect of strength training failure is too stringent a word. However there is no doubt lack of planning will certainly impede maximal results.

What is planning?

Modern strength training concepts are built on a principle of periodisation.

Modern strength training concepts are built on a principle of periodisation. This means that the volume, intensity and type are grouped into cycles. In most instances these cycles are arranged to bring an athlete to peak performance several times a year, depending on the number of major competitions in the yearly cycle. For example an experienced track and field athlete, weightlifter or cyclist may have two major cycles a year with the national/international championships the major goal as far as 'peaking' is concerned. The secondary goal may be a competition of lesser calibre such as a state championship. These cycles in turn are generally subdivided into phases (or micro cycles) such as preparatory, power, competitive and transition.

Some sports use more cycles than others and it is during these various segments that there is considerable variance in the structure of the training program.

This brings us to the question of football and periodisation. The answer is that it is an extremely difficult activity to 'peak' for as unlike most sports where there is a comparatively small number of maximal performances per year, football has a 'peak', i.e. the game, every week. This continues for as much as four to five consecutive months, depending on the level of the football. To further complicate this process of periodisation, the game has many physical aspects (strength and power, skill and agility, speed and endurance) to be integrated into the overall plan.

Furthermore a high degree of anaerobic endurance (the ability to make repeated short sprints with minimal recovery) and a reasonable aerobic capacity (the ability to move up and down the field of play at a steady pace with minimum fatigue) are prerequisites for successful football. However what adds even more to the complexity of the situation is that large quantities of anaerobic/aerobic training are counterproductive to maximal strength and power development.

Periodisation of training for football

Periodisation of football consists of three cycles—the off season, preseason and the competition.

Periodisation can be broken down into three periods (or cycles) over a calendar year—the off season, preseason and competition. The off season generally commences in September and continues until January at elite levels and perhaps a little longer at lesser levels. Preseason ranges from January/February to March/April and then it is competition right through till mid to late August.

Preseason training usually involves intensive anaerobic/aerobic activities at least three to four times a week together with some trial games towards the end of this period. The training usually consists of endurance runs, four hundred metre interval running, short and long sprints, activity drills, circuit training emphasising both strength and fitness, together with a certain amount of skills practice.

Once the competitive phase commences, there is a series of weekly peaks where players have to perform up to expectations or face the likelihood of relegation. This weekly peaking usually takes the form of a pyramid (see Fig. 7.1) with each training session virtually a micro cycle.

In addition to the pyramid of weekly team training activities, at elite levels the players are expected to engage in a certain amount of individual training (maintenance strength training).

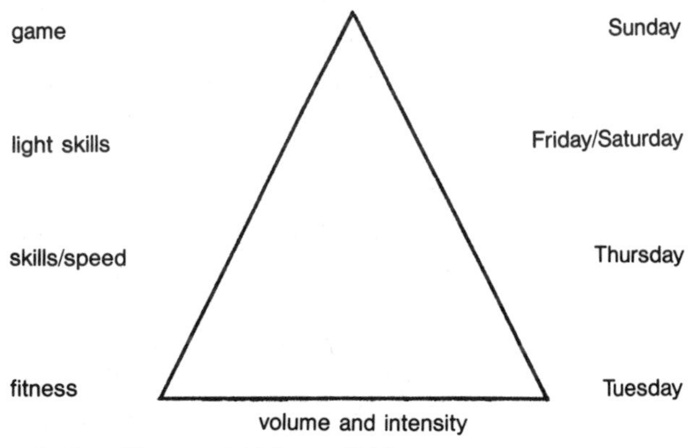

Fig. 7.1 Pyramid of weekly team training activities

Maximising strength training in the yearly calendar

The period most conducive to maximising strength and power is the off season.

A summation of the complex activities involved in preparation for and playing football on a seasonal basis leads to one inescapable conclusion—*The period that is most conducive to maximising strength and power is the off season.* It is during this limited time span (ranging from twelve to fifteen weeks) that the player can apply himself to strength/power development without the inhibitory effect of large volumes of both anaerobic and aerobic training. This is not to say that in the preseason it is impossible to improve strength and power. However as a general rule progress in this field will be minimal, particularly with less genetically endowed players.

While it is important that during the preseason and particularly the competition period strength training remains a continuous part of the overall yearly plan, because of the volume of work required in other facets during these phases, the overall volume of strength training must be diminished. Practical experience would dictate two to three training sessions per week in the preseason. During the competition, certainly the most physically stressful time of the year, it would be unrealistic to expect the player to be able to cope with anything more than two sessions per week. The exception to this is at elite levels, where a professional player with minimal external work commitments is in a position to engage in more extensive 'in season' training.

From personal observation most coaches and players include some strength training (often misguided) in the off season and preseason. However a sense of apathy seems to prevail in regard to 'maintenance' (in season) strength training during the competition. Indeed in some quarters the word resistance could be substituted for apathy. This train of thought is totally archaic.

The importance of maintenance training cannot be overemphasised.

What is overlooked is that strength training is similar to fitness training. It should be specific and is of a transient nature. In other words cessation brings about rapid diminishment. If a player abandons strength training in the competition, his strength levels will begin to deteriorate after about ten days and by four to six weeks a major portion of the off season gains will be lost. Indeed towards the end of the competition (the crucial part if a team has aspirations to excellence) this loss of strength could become critical in winning or losing. *The importance of maintenance training cannot be overemphasised. Without it there is almost total negation of previously accrued benefits.*

It is an interesting fact that at elite levels of football one may read in the media that a certain star player has been reprimanded or even relegated to a lower grade because of unsatisfactory fitness levels. Yet one never observes the same situation in regard to strength training. This is not only an anomaly, but also totally wrong. Furthermore, a player can maintain reasonable strength levels with as little as two 45 minute sessions per week.

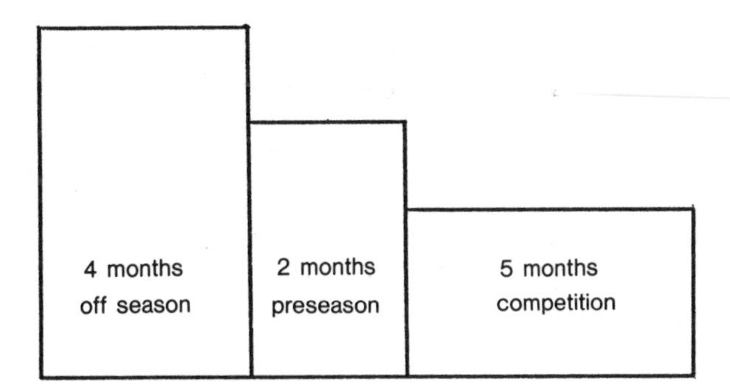

Fig. 7.2 Volume of strength training

Cessation of training brings about rapid diminishment.

In summary, the time for maximal strength and power gains is in the off season, during which both anaerobic and aerobic activities should be restricted to several sessions per week of sprint training or team activities such as basketball or touch football. However a certain volume of strength training (of a diminishing nature) should be an ongoing situation throughout the preseason and competition. There should also be a transition period (rest) of about two to three weeks at the conclusion of the competition in order for the players to recuperate from the wear and tear of the year.

Programming and the individual player

As was mentioned in an earlier unit various genetic factors play a substantial part in effort put out for return generated. In essence some individuals are more fortunate than others in the development of strength and power. Also the physical requisites of players vary greatly. It is important that a player, when assessing his needs, also recognises his weaknesses and adjusts his overall program accordingly.

Broadly speaking players can be divided into three categories relative to strength training requirements for football. Category one is those players who wish to increase strength and power without any consequential increase in muscle mass. The second is those who not only need more strength/power but also increased lean muscle mass. Finally the third category is the players who because of their body type have a tendency to increase bodyfat in the off season—particularly if their nutritional habits are a bit wayward. Consequently while increased strength/power is desirable, a considerably higher content of anaerobic/aerobic activities (compared to the other two categories) will occupy their off season training program.

Understanding the structure of a program

The set system A repetition (R) means the execution of a movement once. It is designated as 1R. 1RM means the maximum amount of resistance that can be used in a particular exercise for one repetition. A collection of repetitions is called a set. It is often written in a quantitative sense as 1 × 10 meaning one set of ten repetitions. Multiple sets (i.e. four) would be written as 4 × 10. In most instances there is a rest interval between sets ranging from two to five minutes. The exception to this is circuit training where the overall format is of a continuous nature.

There are a number of methods of performing sets and repetitions in a weight training program. Each accentuates a particular aspect with all having merit. The three systems that are of major importance to strength training for football are the plateau, step and pyramid set systems.

The plateau set system This simply means a sequence of sets are performed up to a specific intensity in an escalating fashion then continued at the same intensity. For example the exerciser would perform the following: 30 kg × 5R, 40 kg × 5R, 50 kg × 5R × 5R. Total number of sets in this instance is five. Another example using seven sets and three repetitions is 30 kg × 3R, 40 kg × 3R, 50 kg × 3R, 55 kg × 3R × 3R × 3R × 3R.

The step set system This is similar to the plateau system except that there is a continual escalation of resistance until a maximum is reached. An example is 30 kg × 5R, 40 kg × 5R, 50 kg × 5R, 60 kg × 5R, 65 kg × 5R.

The pyramid set system Once again this is an escalating system of repetitions and sets. However at the lower end of the scale of resistance the repetitions are of greater magnitude (as against the same repetitions right across the board in previous systems). As the resistance increases the repetitions decrease. An example of this is 30 kg × 10R, 40 kg × 7R, 45 kg × 5R, 50 kg × 3R, 55 kg × 1/2R.

A more advanced method of this system is to include one or two 'drop back' sets, i.e. in the above example after the set on 55 kg for 1 or 2R, the weight would be reduced to 45 kg for 4R for one or two sets before finally reducing it to 35 kg for a further 7R. Obviously there would be an increase in the fatigue/volume factor with the addition of extra sets. Variations of the pyramid system are generally favoured where both increased strength and muscle size are to be developed in parallel.

If the muscle fibre recruitment graph and repetition continuum (Figs 7.3 and 7.4) are examined a number of conclusions can be drawn:

Strength and power are best developed with lesser repetitions using greater resistance.

(a) Strength and power are best developed with lesser repetitions using greater resistance. It should also be kept in mind that speed is also a factor in power (speed of execution is important).

(b) Hypertrophy of fast twitch fibres is best achieved in the 5 to 10 repetition range. This also has a positive effect on strength production. Hypertrophy of slow twitch fibres escalates in higher ranges of repetitions with diminishing effect on increased strength.

As a point of interest examination of the intensity of work graph will reveal that in the zone of maximum intensity there is maximal recruitment

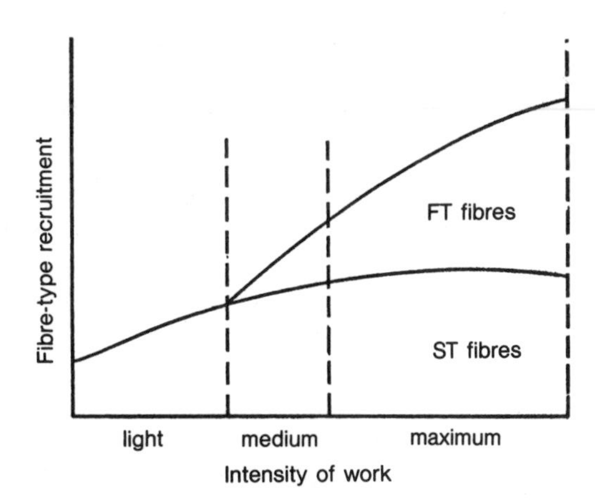

Fig. 7.3 Muscle fibre recruitment graph relating repetitions and intensity to strength and size

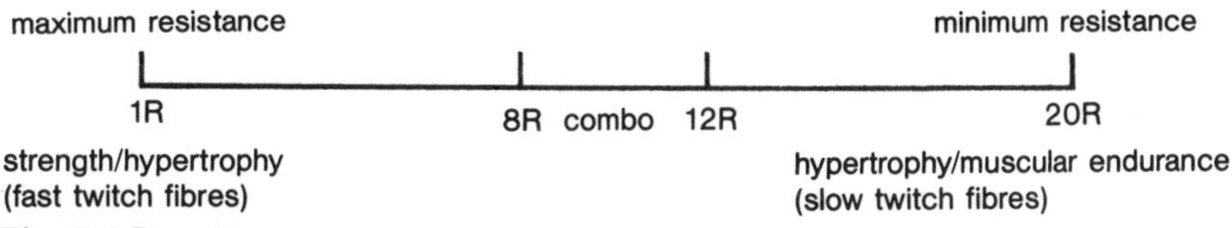

Fig. 7.4 Repetition continuum

of all fibre types as against only minor fast twitch involvement in the moderate zone. In the zone of light work intensity there is zero fast twitch involvement.

Taking into consideration the above, the following parameters can be established for the varied requirements of football players.

For strength and power development

This is best developed in the range of repetitions from as little as 1–2 up to 5–6. There would be minimal hypertrophy of muscle unless multiple sets of 5–6 repetitions were performed, in which case some muscle gain could be expected if coupled with appropriate nutrition. The likelihood of hypertrophy under these conditions would be greater in mesomorphic body types. Listed below are some examples for a particular exercise using the previously described set systems:

Step system: 40 kg × 3, 50 kg × 3, 55 kg × 3, 60 kg × 3, 62.5 kg × 3.
Plateau system: 40 kg × 3, 50 kg × 3, 55 kg × 3 × 3 × 3 × 3 × 3.
Plateau system: 40 kg × 5, 45 kg × 5, 50 kg × 5 × 5 × 5 × 5.
Pyramid system: 40 kg × 6, 45 kg × 5, 50 kg × 3, 57 kg × 2, 62.5 kg × 1, 55 kg × 2, 50 kg × 4.

Resistance would range from 55 to 60% of 1RM with the initial sets up to as much as 90% 1RM depending on the repetitions.

It should be remembered that when performing the exercises the accent should be on speed of movement without sacrificing correct technique. As previously mentioned the eccentric part of the exercise should be carried out in a slow and purposeful manner.

Combination of muscle hypertrophy and strength/power

Taking into consideration that muscle hypertrophy in power sports such as football should be aimed at fast twitch muscle fibres, the repetition range would be from 8/10 with less resistance, descending to 2/3 for heavier sets.

Pyramid system: 35 kg × 10, 40 kg × 8, 45 kg × 6, 50 kg × 3 × 3, 40 kg × 7.
Combination step/pyramid system: (a) 35 kg × 10, 40 kg × 8, 45 kg × 6 × 6 × 6. (b) 35 kg × 10, 40 kg × 8, 45 kg × 6, 40 kg × 8, 35 kg × 10.

With the above system, power exercises such as power cleans and snatches have minimal effect on muscle hypertrophy and so maximum repetitions for these movements would be 5.

The only exception to this would be in circuit training where higher repetitions could be used to induce both muscular and cardiorespiratory fatigue. This will be more fully discussed in a later part of this chapter.

Loading—the varying of resistance and its effects

The training stress must be of a continuously increasing magnitude.

The process by which the muscular system adapts to a particular stress and elicits a change in strength and composition is generally referred to as the progressive overload system. This means that for improvement in strength training to be of an ongoing nature the training stress (volume and intensity) must be of a continuously increasing magnitude. When the body adapts to a particular work load, to induce further improvement the volume and/or intensity must be increased.

This leads to the question of whether one should train to failure at each workout or in gym jargon 'train heavy every session'. There is no doubt that training to maximum or failure at each workout will produce results over a short period of time. However even in the most gifted of people the body's ultimate reaction to this type of training is physiological and psychological fatigue with a consequential plateauing (and in some cases retardment) of progress. Scientific studies coupled with empirical observations have established the best way to maintain progress in strength training. Over an extended period of time the answer is to vary the training intensity and volume of workouts using various forms of cycling.

Cycling of intensity

The practice of cycling the various forms of training throughout the year has been mentioned above. The same principle is used to vary resistance.

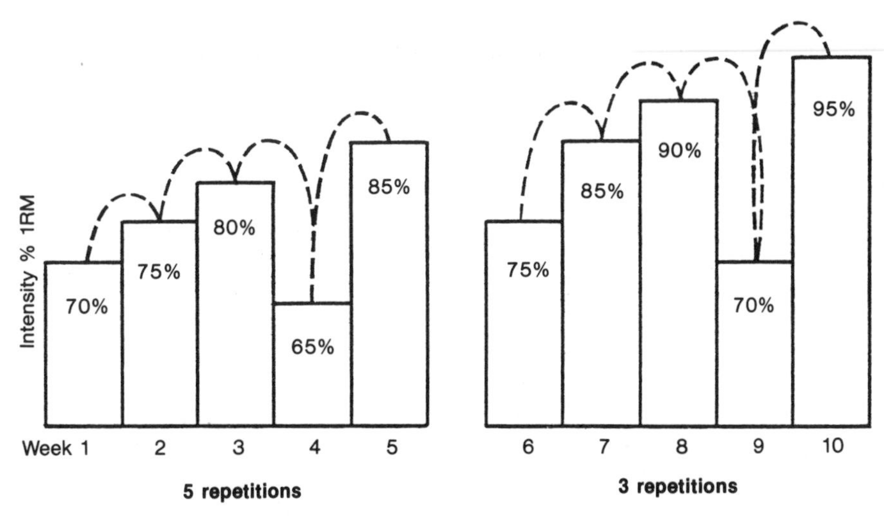

Fig. 7.5 The block system of varying work load

The cycles can be simple, such as heavy, medium and light.

The cycles can be simple, such as a heavy, medium and light workout each week. However even training heavy/to failure once a week over a lengthy period can sometimes be excessively fatiguing. Another simple system is to alternate heavy and light weeks. This method of variation is ideal for the novice.

What is considered a more efficient method for experienced exercisers is to group together a series of weeks of varying levels of volume and intensity of work load, i.e. light, medium and heavy weeks, in a 'wave-like' escalating fashion. This is often referred to as the 'block' system, an elementary example of which is illustrated schematically above. This example covers a total of ten weeks but can easily be adapted to shorter or longer periods.

The program shown in Fig. 7.5 would be ideal for the player training for strength/power with minimum concern for muscle hypertrophy. Weeks 1–5 involve sets of five repetitions, followed by weeks 6–10 using sets of three repetitions. On the lower intensity weeks (65–80%) the plateau set system would be appropriate, with the higher intensity weeks (85–95%) using the step set system.

In order to clarify the above, listed below are some examples of various weeks using the power clean as a model (1RM = 100 kg).

Week 1—50 kg × 5, 60 kg × 5, 70 kg × 5 × 5 × 5 × 5.
Week 2—50 kg × 5, 60 kg × 5, 70 kg × 5, 75 kg × 5 × 5 × 5.
Week 3—50 kg × 5, 60 kg × 5, 70 kg × 5, 80 kg × 5 × 5 × 5.
Week 4—50 kg × 5, 60 kg × 5, 65 kg × 5 × 5 × 5 × 5.
Week 5—50 kg × 5, 60 kg × 5, 70 kg × 5, 80 kg × 5, 85 kg × 5.
Week 6—50 kg × 3, 60 kg × 3, 70 kg × 3, 75 kg × 3 × 3 × 3 × 3.

Week 7—50 kg × 3, 60 kg × 3, 70 kg × 3, 80 kg × 3, 85 kg × 3 × 3 × 3.
Week 8—50 kg × 3, 60 kg × 3, 70 kg × 3, 80 kg × 3, 85 kg × 3, 90 kg × 3 × 3.
Week 9—50 kg × 3, 60 kg × 3, 70 kg × 3 × 3 × 3 × 3 × 3.
Week 10—60 kg × 3, 70 kg × 3, 80 kg × 3, 90 kg × 3, 95 kg × 3 × 3, 85 kg × 3.

This ten week period could be followed by a four week phase using double and single repetitions with intensities of 85–97–80–105%, with a target in week four of new personal bests (105% or higher).

With the 'block' system, on high intensity weeks (85% or greater) that intensity is only used twice a week, assuming training consists of three sessions per week. On the other training day a 10% reduction in intensity should be adopted using the plateau system.

The 'block system' should only be used in conjunction with multiple joint/multi muscle group movements such as the squat, power clean and power snatch, together with major pressing exercises such as bench pressing and press/push press overhead. For other movements variations of heavy, medium and light are more suitable.

Prior to commencing the 'block system' the exerciser should ascertain his 1RM. This is necessary in order to quantify percentages.

The exercises and arranging a program

So far the system of sets, repetitions, volume and intensity, together with the cycling of these components, has been thoroughly explored. The next step is to examine the arranging of the various exercises into a logical order to form a training program.

All programs should feature total body movements.

First and foremost on all programs should be total body movements (core exercises). Relative to football they are power cleans, power snatches and back squats. Following total body movements the muscle groups of the upper and lower body are exercised in the following order—shoulders, upper back, chest, arms, neck, stomach, lower back and calves.

Shoulders, chest and upper back are always exercised before arms. When performing compound exercises for these large muscle groups the arms are a connecting link and, if previously fatigued, will be unable to handle sufficient resistance to adequately stress the muscle groups for which the exercises were primarily designed. For example if bicep curls are performed before chinning the bar, the fact that the arm flexors are pre exhausted will limit the number of chins that can be performed as against without pre stressing the arm flexors. Conversely chinning prior to arm curls does not greatly affect the amount of resistance for arm flexor movements.

This principle also applies to triceps and either bench pressing or overhead pressing. Broadly speaking, in upper body compound exercises the arm flexors are the connecting link for pulling movements, the triceps for pushing movements. Another factor to be considered when arranging a program where brevity is a major factor, is that the arms are adequately exercised by all compound upper body exercises (as well as power cleans/snatches). Therefore in these circumstances direct arm exercises could be omitted. In the same vein squats and power cleans involve many smaller muscle groups such as mid torso, calves etc.

In summary one could liken the body to a 'power chain' with the chain being exercised as a unit, to be followed by the individual links (an holistic approach). However the first priority is to the 'power chain' as a composite unit.

Training frequency

Strength training in the off season should be carried out three to four times a week.

As a broad rule for football where in most instances some other form of training is carried out in parallel (speed fitness), strength training should be carried out in the off season three/four times a week on alternate days. During the preseason and competition, training frequency will vary and this is fully discussed under maintenance training.

Some sample programs

Schedule A	Schedule B
Power clean	Power clean
Squat	Squat
Press behind neck	Overhead dumbell pressing
Barbell or dumbell rowing	Upright rowing
Bench press	Lat machine pull downs
Barbell curl	Incline bench press
Sit ups	Dumbell curls
Partner resistance neck	Triceps press on lat machine
Leg curls	Four way neck with headstrap
Calf raises	Good mornings
Back raises	Reverse trunk twist

Schedules A and B cover a wide cross section of exercises. A disadvantage of this is that in excess of three sets with perhaps four in core exercises would be inappropriate due to time and energy constrains. Both schedules would be suitable for novice exercisers (a preparatory phase) performing two/three sets per exercise.

Schedule A could be used for six weeks followed by Schedule B for the same period of time. Schedule A would involve repetitions of 8–10 for all exercises using training poundage intensities based on heavy–medium–light weeks. The exception would be power cleans where five repetitions would be more appropriate. For the novice the first three weeks of the initial six weeks of Schedule A would consists of two sets of ten repetitions using an intensity (load) of approximately three repetitions short of failure in each set.

Schedule B would consist of three sets of eight repetitions for all exercises except squat and power clean which would be four sets of five repetitions. Intensity in this schedule would be based on alternate heavy and light weeks. There may be a need for exercise substitution, i.e. replacing a movement with a similar one. This would depend upon training environment and equipment availability.

Further sample programs (advanced)

Schedule C
Power clean
Squat
Dumbell press
Chins or dumbell rowing
Bench press
4 way neck with head strap
Twisting sit ups

Schedule D
Leg press with calf extension
Power clean and dumbell press
Barbell rowing
Parallel bar dips
Barbell curl
Sit ups—crunches
Back raises

Schedule E
Bench step ups with dumbells
Power snatch
Press behind neck
Upright rowing
Lat machine pulldowns
Reverse trunk twists
Parallel bar dips

The common factor, apart from balance, of Schedules C, D and E is their comparative brevity (relative to A and B). The advantage of this is that it allows the exerciser to perform five to seven sets on each movement and still keep within the constraints of time and energy (5/7 core movements—5 mid torso/neck).

Schedules C, D and E are for players who have completed several off season periods on Schedules A and B or who have had previous weight training experience. In terms of repetitions and loading intensities much will depend on whether the aim of the exerciser is non hypertrophic strength and power or strength and power together with increased lean muscle mass. These options have previously been discussed.

Schedule C is the base workout. It can be adopted to either strength and power or strength, power and muscle hypertrophy. This would be dependent upon sets, repetitions and intensities. While C is effective on its own, Schedules D and E are more 'support' programs best suited for combining with C as shown below:

Option 1

	Week 1			*Week 2*	
Day 1	Day 2	Day 3	Day 1	Day 2	Day 3
C	D	C	D	C	D

Repeat pattern over a six to eight week period.

Option 2

Substitute Schedule E for D in Option 1.

A third and slightly more advanced option is to train every alternate day. In other words there are seven workouts per fortnight rather than six on the three times a week basis.

A good combination off season training program for an experienced (in weight training) player would be a two to three week preparatory phase using either Schedule A or B, followed by a six week phase on C and a further six weeks on either Option 1 or 2.

Further advanced schedules

Up to this stage the programs have been based on alternate day training—either three times a week or seven times a fortnight. However for those players who desire to increase their training load either because (a) their overall progress has ceased or (b) they seek an increase in their current rate of improvement, a more advanced schedule may be attempted. This type of training should not be necessary in the first one/two years where alternate day training should suffice. Indeed many players may never need to work out (strength training) more frequently than three sessions a week.

On the basis of four sessions a week, training days can be (a) Monday, Tuesday, Thursday, Saturday (b) Monday, Wednesday, Friday, Saturday or (c) Monday, Tuesday, Thursday, Friday. Below is an example of a four day a week program. Substitution of exercises may be necessary in some instances depending on equipment availability.

Schedule F

Day 1	*Day 2*	*Day 3*	*Day 4*
Power clean	Power snatch	Power clean	Leg press
Back squat	Leg press	Back squat	Lat machine
Dumbell press	Bench press	Dumbell press	Bench press
Upright rowing	Lat machine	Forward rowing	Leg curls
Parallel bar dips	Leg curls	Parallel bar dips	Upright rowing
Dumbell curl	Reverse trunk twists	Dumbell curl	Back raises
Neck	Back raises	Neck	

An ideal off season program involving Schedule F would be a three week preparatory phase on either Schedule A or B, to be followed by six weeks on Schedule C, and finally six weeks on Schedule F. On this combined program (in order to provide variety) press behind the neck could be susbtituted for dumbell press in Schedule F. Load intensity, sets (type), repetitions, etc. would adhere to principles previously outlined.

Preparatory phase

Reference has already been made to the novice and Schedules A and B. However the experienced strength trainer who has just completed an arduous football season will have, at the best, indulged in some maintenance training in the later stages of the competition. This is followed by several well earned rest weeks to allow the body to recuperate from the wear and tear of the season. Therefore a short preparatory phase should be incorporated before resuming training on the more advanced schedules. This phase need be no longer than three weeks and either Schedule A or B using three/four sets of 8 to 10 repetitions would be adequate. Intensity should be relatively easy—on the heaviest set at the completion of the final repetiition there should be a couple of reps 'in hand'.

Maintenance (in season) training

Much has already been said about the importance of maintenance (in season) training. Taking into consideration constraints of time due to other aspects of physical preparation in the preseason and competition, brevity and intelligent selection of exercises are the key to success in this area.

If time permits Schedule C once a week and alternation of Schedules D and E for the other weekly session would be effective. Four to five sets would suffice while loading could be based on alternate heavy and light weeks. Where time is really at a premium a short schedule of power clean, squat and dumbell overhead press for five sets of five to eight repetitions could be completed in about forty minutes or even less if performed as a weight circuit. Variation and balance can also be achieved by substituting leg press, power snatch and bench press every alternate workout. At elite levels, the professional player may utilise more complex cyclic methods during the 'in season' competition period. This is best implemented under the tutelage of an experienced strength-training coach, whereby individual needs can be incorporated into the program design.

In the competition season power exercises affecting the legs such as squats, power cleans/snatches, leg presses, etc. should be confined to three to five repetitions. This will assist in preventing excessive fatigue in the legs due to the demands of playing and training. In terms of leg fatigue, lower repetitions rather than lower intensity is the key to prevention. Some coaches erroneously promulgate the principle of *only* lighter weights and higher repetitions in the playing season. Higher repetitions are okay for the upper body, particularly for individuals who struggle to maintain muscle mass due to the rigours of competition.

Some coaches erroneously promulgate the principle of* only *lighter weights in the playing season.

Speed training

Speed and the factors involving its development have already been discussed in Chapter 2. The majority of football coaches and trainers incorporate some form of speed training in the preseason and playing season. However most players would benefit by adding sprint training to their off season strength program.

Most players would benefit by adding sprint training to their off season program.

This could take place on alternate days to weight training at the local park or golf course (dodging golf balls is one way to 'sharpen up'!). The training should include some sprint drills, together with 'power' work such as short hill sprints (both incline and decline) and plyometrics. If available, players would also benefit from joining an athletics club or sprint class under the tutelage of a competent coach.

For players who fall into the category of big, bulky and sometimes off season 'fatties' (endomorphic traits) the feasibility of sprint training in the off season is arguable. Off season training for this type of individual is specifically outlined in a later part of this chapter.

Circuit training

Circuit training is a program of specific exercises (known as stations) arranged in a particular order and performed in a continuous manner, i.e. no rest periods between exercises. The number of exercises, type and length of training varies, depending on the physical factors the circuit is designed to emphasise. Most circuits embody some element of strength, strength endurance and cardiorespiratory fitness. While this form of training is very much about achieving a reasonable degree of overall physical proficiency in a comparatively short space of training time, i.e. thirty to forty minutes, one fact should not be overlooked—that the various physical aspects of strength and cardiorespiratory fitness can be more effectively developed by separate training. This of course requires a much greater time commitment.

Structure and performance of circuit training

There are many combinations of exercises that can be used to form a circuit. They range from simple movements involving bodyweight only (i.e. push ups, step ups, burpees and jumps, chins, sit ups etc.) which are ideal for performing at the training oval, to more complex circuits involving free weights and other resistance modes specific to a well equipped gymnasium.

Irrespective of the type of circuit, one of the most important factors in its design is the selection and order of performance of exercises. In terms of football, first priority is movements involving multiple muscle groups (total body movements). The rationale for this is that apart from the fact that most aspects of football require major muscle group

There should be an intermingling of stress and recovery exercises.

involvement, this type of exercise places great stress upon the cardiorespiratory system.

Examples of this group of exercises are power cleans, power snatches, squats, bench step ups, burpees and jumps, 10 to 15 metre shuttle runs, squat jumps, clean and press bar or dumbells in a continuous manner, chinning and double and single leg hopping. However because of the extremely stressful nature of these movements there is a need to intersperse them with less demanding exercises. Examples of this group (recovery movements) are various forms of sit ups, leg raises, back raises and to a lesser extent bench press, upright rowing and curls.

The overall arrangement of exercises is critical in circuit training.

The overall arrangement of the two groups of exercises is most important. The basic principle is that there be a rotation of major muscle groups. What that means in essence is that if a particular muscle group is involved in too many consecutive exercises there will be a temporary cessation of the circuit due to localised muscle fatigue. For instance squats followed by burpees, jumps and step ups would fatigue the legs to the point that the exerciser would have to temporarily call a halt to the circuit. This is contrary to the aim of the circuit—in order to sufficiently stress the cardiorespiratory system to elicit greater efficiency there should be continuity of activity for at least twenty minutes and up to forty for football.

Guidelines for designing and performing a circuit

1. As a general rule, after two to three stress exercises, a recovery exercise should be performed.

2. Ten to fourteen exercises is ideal and they should be repeated two to three times.

3. There should be a gradual build up of volume. For instance the first week—one round of the circuit, second week—one and a half rounds, third week—two rounds etc. This build up may vary depending on individual fitness.

4. The intensity of each exercise should be about 60/70% of maximum performance. For example—if burpees and jumps maximum repetitions to failure is 30 then circuit intensity would be 18 to 21. Bench step ups—maximum to failure is 40 repetitions then circuit intensity is 24 to 28 repetitions. Power cleans—maximum weight for ten repetitions is 60 kg then circuit intensity would be 35 to 45 kg. Agility sprints are generally repeated six to ten times at maximum speed.

5. The first one/two sessions of the first week should be solely devoted to testing in order to establish the intensity of the circuit.

The motto for circuit training is 'no pain no gain'.

6. After a period of time (which will vary on an individual basis) an adaption will take place and the exerciser will become fitter and stronger. Consequently the original intensity, which was inducing great fatigue and respiratory stress by the conclusion of the circuit, will no longer achieve

Fig. 7.6 Burpees

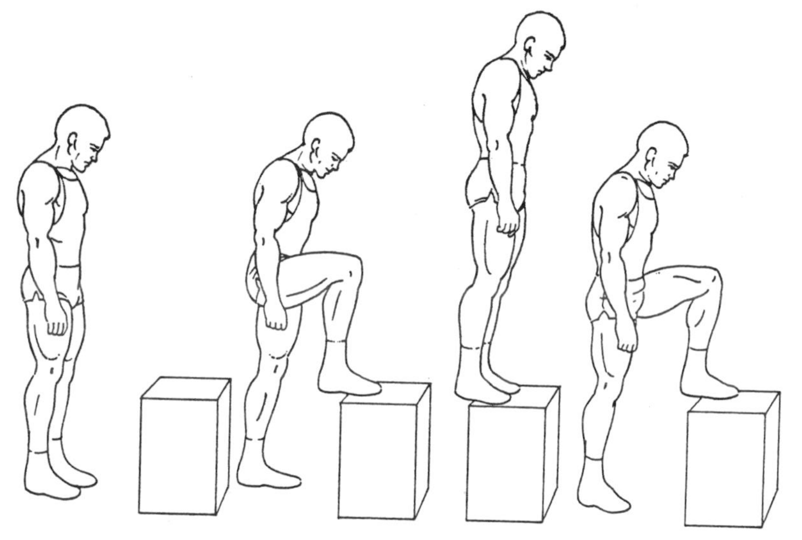

Fig. 7.7 Bench stepping

this effect. Therefore for ongoing progression the intensity will need to be increased.

This can be achieved in a number of ways:

(a) Increasing the length of the circuit. This can be accomplished by either adding more exercises or increasing the intensity of the original circuit, i.e. more reps and/or more weight resistance.

(b) Maintaining the same overall intensity and endeavouring to complete the original circuit in a shorter time.

(c) An extension of (a) would be to increase the length of the circuit by completing an additional round, i.e. three repeats instead of two, four instead of three. Practical experience would dictate that for any circuit of consequential length (ten/twelve exercises) four rounds would be the maximum.

7. Because of the physiological stresses involved in circuit training (the motto is 'you've gotta love pain') it is desirable to train with a partner(s). This has the effect of both encouragement and competition. Should there be a scarcity of equipment, i.e. only one Olympic weightlifting bar, step up bench etc., it may be necessary for the first person to complete three or four exercises before the partner commences. This can have the added competitive effect of the second person trying to narrow the gap and conversely the first person endeavouring to widen it.

Some examples of a general circuit specific to football

C1 (general)	
Burpees and jumps	
Power snatch	10R
Agility sprints	
Sit ups	
Power clean	10R
Bench step ups	
Back raises	
Agility sprints	
Dumbell press	10R
Chins/forward rowing	10R
Leg raises	
Squat jumps	
Bench press	10R

C2 (general)	
Punching heavy bag	1 minute
Agility sprints	
Power clean	5R
Sit ups	
Burpees and jumps	
Power snatch	5R
Reverse trunk twist	
Squat or leg press	5R
Dumbell press	5R
Knee tuck jumps	
Upright rowing	5R
Bench press	5R
Back raises	10R

C3 (oval environment)

- Push ups
- Agility sprints
- Sit ups
- Wrestling (partner push/pull)
- Park bench step ups
- Leg raises
- Cone sprints
- Squat jumps
- Reverse push ups
- Double leg hops 10–15 metres
- Knee to chest sit ups
- Burpees and jumps
- Reverse trunk twist
- Agility sprints

C4 (running oriented)	
Power cleans	5R
Agility sprints	
Sit ups	
Bench press	8R
Agility sprints	
Knee to chest sit ups	
Power snatch	5R
Single leg hops 10–15 metres	
Back raises	
Agility sprints	
Bench step ups	
Dumbell press	8R
Reverse trunk twist	
Cone sprints	
Sit ups	

Medicine ball exercise with a partner can provide additional variety.

There are many other variations that can be improvised depending on available equipment. For instance various medicine ball exercises with a partner can provide additional variety and they are easily transported into an outside environment. The important thing is to adhere to design principles as outlined in this chapter.

Group circuit training

Where large numbers of persons are involved (i.e. several football teams) circuit training is best conducted on a circular rotational basis. What this means is that the stations (exercises) of the circuit are arranged in a circle (see below) and, depending on the overall numbers, two to three persons are allocated to each station. The coach/trainer then signals the entire group to commence exercising. Each station is carried out on a time basis, usually thirty seconds. At the conclusion of the allocated time a signal is given to stop. Immediately the groups on each station move to the next station and the procedure is repeated until the entire circuit is completed by every player. Depending on the number of exercises, the circuit is repeated two to four times.

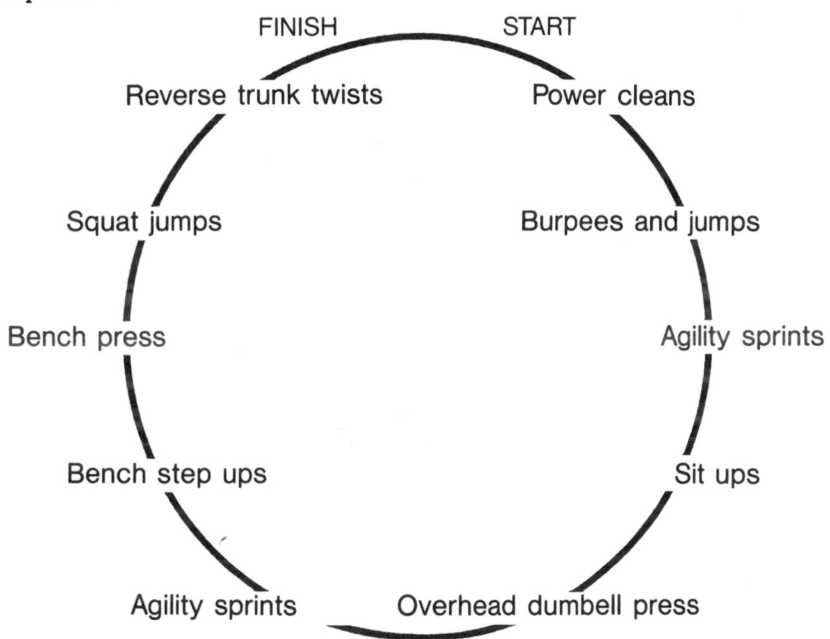

While this is the most viable procedure for group circuit training, it has a number of pitfalls compared to its individual/partner counterpart. First it requires considerable equipment and space and any more than two/three persons to a station is impractical. Secondly and more importantly, because of the varying levels of strength and fitness of each individual, a specific time on a certain station may be easy for some and very difficult for others. For example exercises like burpees and jumps, step ups, knee tuck jumps and the like favour the lighter person while

An entire team can train simultaneously with group circuit training.

strength related movements are more suited to the heavier, stronger individual. There is no total answer to this problem as the time spent at each station must be the same in order for continuous rotation. Arranging groups in body types partially alleviates the situation. The greatest asset of group circuit training is that an entire team can train simultaneously on the same training format.

Circuit weight training

Up to this point the context of circuit training has revolved around circuit stations consisting of a combination of weight movements, explosive calisthenic type bodyweight exercises and agility sprints. A variation of the above is what is termed circuit weight training, which involves only weight exercises for all stations.

The principles previously outlined for general circuits in regard to order of exercise and intensity apply equally for circuit weight training. If the repetitions are restricted to five the circuit will become more strength oriented while in the higher range of repetitions (eight to fifteen) the emphasis will shift towards muscle hypertrophy and strength endurance. While there will be some cardiorespiratory involvement in this type of circuit, the benefits in this area are considerably less than in a more general circuit of the type previously discussed.

Another modified form of this type of training is one popularised by some leading bodybuilders over a decade ago. It is known as PHA (peripheral heart action) training and consists of grouping exercises for three or four different body parts and performing a set of repetitions on each before resting briefly and then repeating the procedure three to five times. In essence PHA training is a form of 'mini' weight circuit.

In the preseason and competition economy of time can be important.

The major value of these forms of circuit weight training is that they accomplish a large volume of training in a comparatively short period of time. However this type of training will not achieve the same strength gains as other methods outlined in this text. The predominant usage of circuit weight training within the context of football is that of maintenance training in the preseason and competition where economy of time can be important.

Example of a weight circuit

Power clean, bench press, curl, back squat, upright rowing, sit ups, power snatch, overhead bar or dumbell press, calf raises, back raises.

The circuit is listed in performance order. Total body movements are interspersed with less stressful (smaller muscle group) exercises. Where possible 'pushing' and 'pulling' movements should be alternated.

Circuit training—its place in yearly periodisation

During the preseason and competition most coaches and/or club trainers will use some form of circuit training as part of the overall training plan. In many instances this will be on a group (team) basis.

In regard to the off season period the persons most suited to circuit training are the individuals who, because of their body type, have a distinct tendency to increase body fat and quickly lose fitness in a non physical environment. For this type of player the off season could be divided into a three week preparatory phase and two six week power/conditioning phases as follows:

Preparatory General circuit Cl or C2, using the three week period to establish circuit intensity and progressive build up to three continuous repeats of the circuit as previously outlined. This should be performed twice a week. Also on separate days from the circuit training, weight schedule A or B is carried out twice a week for three/four sets of five to eight repetitions.

Power/conditioning phases—duration six weeks each

Phase 1	*Phase 2*
General circuit C1 or C2 (twice weekly)	General circuit C4
Weight schedule C (twice weekly)	Weight schedule C (once weekly)
Team ball game such as basketball/touch football (once/twice weekly)	Fartlek style run (once/twice weekly)

Some guidelines for the above:
Weight schedule C should not be performed on the same day as circuit training. Other aerobic activities (i.e. basketball, Fartlek) can be performed after Schedule C if so desired. Sets and repetitions for Schedule C in Phase 1 should be 5 × 5. Phase 2 would be 6/7 × 3 with intensity as per previously outlined 'block' system. Weight schedule C in Phase 2 would achieve a superior result if performed twice weekly. This would depend on time and commitment. Fartlek style run is best performed over a terrain that has some hills. This type of running consists of a mixture of slow pace work interspersed with short sprints and occasional short rest periods (walk recovery).

Strength training for the younger person

As a general guideline most youngsters could commence weight training at thirteen to fourteen years of age.

A question often asked by concerned parents is what age should their son commence strength training for football. This is difficult to answer without seeing the individual concerned because the onset of physical maturity can vary considerably from one youngster to another. In most instances a general guideline would be around thirteen to fourteen years.

In terms of the principles of programming, most of what has already been said also applies to strength training for youngsters. However the following additional guidelines should take precedence:

1. Youngsters should be under correct instruction and supervision, with great care taken to ensure proper exercise technique.

2. If possible they should train in the company of other persons.

Closely adhere to all safety principles.

3. All safety principles should be closely adhered to, which includes checking collars on bars are securely affixed, benches are structurally sound, pulley wires are not frayed, etc. This particularly applies to home training, which is often the mode adopted by youngsters.

4. It is important that weight training is treated as a serious matter (no skylarking).

Youngsters should train under skilled supervision.

5. For the first six months twice weekly training sessions are sufficient based on alternate six week rotations of Schedules A and B, using three to four sets of six to ten repetitions (pyramid system). Taking into consideration the inherent desire of youngsters to see how much stronger they have become, 1RM should be restricted to every twelve weeks and performed under supervision. The key in these circumstances is for the supervisor to judge when the point of 1RM is reached and not precede beyond to failure (in other words one should err on the side of caution). It is important that, irrespective of intensity, continual training to failure be avoided. Simply put, at the conclusion of each set, regardless of repetitions and resistance, the youngster should have a reserve of strength sufficient to perform a couple of extra repetitions.

6. In the off season period, which is usually much longer in schoolboy football, youngsters should be encouraged to take part in other physical activities. Athletics (competing in sprints, jumps and throws), basketball and swimming are ideal. This leads to a more complete overall physical development at this stage of a young person's growth.

7. Instill in the young person the importance of neck training for the remainder his playing career. Partner resistance movements should be encouraged initially before progressing onto more intense weight resistance exercises.

Some final thoughts on programming

1. The principle of heavy–medium–light intensity has frequently been mentioned in this chapter. This can be expressed in percentages such as:

Heavy	100%	× designated repetitions
Medium	90–85%	× same repetitions
Light	85–80%	× same repetitions

Heavy intensity could be defined as training almost up to the point of failure (and on some occasions to failure) for a specific number of repetitions. Using the amount of resistance for heavy intensity as a yardstick, medium intensity would be 7.5 to 10 kg less for the same number of repetitions. Light intensity would consistute 15 to 20 kg less than the heavy intensity. For exercises involving smaller, weaker muscle groups this margin between intensities would be less.

As the individual becomes stronger, the variance becomes greater especially in the total body, multiple joint movements. Quantitative examples would be as follows:

Exercise—power clean/squat/bench press, etc.

Heavy intensity	60 kg × 5	110 kg × 5	130 kg × 5
Medium	52.5 kg × 5	100 kg × 5	115 kg × 5
Light	45 kg × 5	90 kg × 5	105 kg × 5

What should be considered is that in most instances only one or two sets are performed on a heavy intensity resistance, whereas multiple sets are generally employed for medium/light intensities.

When considering percentage (%) of 1RM, figures outlined in this text are approximate. An athlete's ability to perform a certain number of repetitions at a particular percentage of 1RM varies between individuals, type of exercise and training experience.

2. At all levels of football the importance of neck training throughout a footballer's career cannot be overemphasised. Apart from a fatality, there is nothing more tragic than a player suffering permanent incapacity through spinal injury. It is an accepted medical fact that neck strengthening can have a most positive influence in preventing this type of injury. Irrespective of the phase of training (off season, preseason, competition), some neck exercises should always be incorporated in the overall training plan. If through time constraints, fatigue or general neglect neck exercises are not performed on the scheduled training day, then include them after sprint training or on a training rest day. They are non fatiguing to the rest of the body and there is no excuse for neglect of this vital aspect.

There are a number of specific exercises for neck development listed in Chapter 6. Also, movements such as the power clean/snatch and upright rowing assist in stabilising the neck area.

Keep a written record of training details.

3. The recording of training schedules in some form of workout book with details regarding type of exercise, frequency of training, sets, repetitions, resistance, etc. is essential for maximising continuity of progress. It should be apparent that if a record is kept of previous years' workouts it is much easier to asssess what was the most beneficial program. It also enables the exerciser to gauge progress (or lack of it) and where necessary make appropriate adjustments to future training schedules.

4. A battery of strength/speed tests (1RM/3RM on power clean, squat, bench press, 40-metre sprint, standing, high and broad jump) should be conducted at (a) conclusion of off season training, (b) various intervals throughout the pre and in season cycles. This information is essential in the assessment of the efficacy of training methodology.

8. Nutrition

It's not the will to win, but it's the will to prepare to win that wins games!

Nutrition is often misunderstood and neglected.

One important aspect of the physical preparation of a footballer is nutrition. Unfortunately this vital area is often misunderstood and neglected. Proper nutrition is not only essential to maximise the benefits of strength training, it also plays a significant role in the areas of cardiorespiratory fitness training and the game itself.

In order to understand the role of nutrition in strength training (and in football in general) one must be familiar with the six elements of nutrition (water, protein, carbohydrates, fats, vitamins and minerals) and the part they play in keeping the body operating at peak physical efficiency.

Water

Water is very important to the proper functioning of the human body (which is largely comprised of water). Indeed while a person can survive for a considerable time without food, such is not the case in regard to water.

Water losses occur daily in a variety of ways and these must be replaced so that a water balance is maintained. The major sources of replacement are water that is drunk and water absorbed from other fluids and foods—fruit and vegetables have a particularly high water content.

Water serves a variety of purposes within the body. It acts as a cleansing agent for the waste products of the various processes that take place in the metabolism of carbohydrates, fats and protein. The importance of protein for strength training will be discussed below. The waste products of protein metabolism are potentially dangerous and so a diet relatively high in protein should be accompanied by a plentiful supply of water.

Water aids in the circulation of the blood.

Water also aids in the circulation of the blood by preventing excessive viscosity. In other words the blood stays thin and circulates freely, thereby keeping vital oxygen supplies in all body tissue, a factor which is very important to the sportsperson. All football players are familiar with loss of water via sweating, whether in the gym or out on the playing field. If this sweat loss is not replaced as soon as possible dire consequences could result.

The ideal way to replace body fluid loss is to drink cool, plain water. The reason for this is that studies of fluid absorption indicate that cold fluids are emptied from the stomach at a significantly faster rate than fluids at body temperature. Also of considerable importance is the observation that gastric emptying is retarded when ingested fluids contain sugar. What this means is that when training in hot weather, and especially when the exercise is intense, don't rehydrate with soft drinks when cool plain water is available. It is also prudent to consume around 300 ml of cool water some fifteen minutes before exercising in hot weather. During the exercise a volume of 200 ml ingested at about fifteen minute intervals is probably a realistic goal for rehydration as larger volumes tend to produce a bloated feeling.

Protein

Adequate protein in the daily food ration plays a significant part in strength training.

Protein could be described as the substance that keeps the various body tissues in good shape. This is very much the situation in respect to muscle tissue. Consequently adequate protein in the daily food ration is important for strength training, assuming even greater significance in the pursuit of increased muscle size.

The foods that are high in protein are generally of animal origin, although some vegetables and grain foods are also reasonable sources of protein (beans, brown rice, corn, wheat products) apart from their primary role as energy producing carbohydrates. However these vegetable proteins are said to be incomplete as compared with protein from animal origin, and so need to be combined with each other during the same meal in a proper combination. For instance brown rice and beans combine to form complete protein, as do corn and beans or lentils.

In relation to strength training the protein value of vegetables and grains should be regarded as a supplement to animal protein and not as a substitute. For example an ideal evening meal for a football player endeavouring to maximise strength training would be grilled fish or chicken with brown rice, lightly steamed beans and corn. Here the rice, beans and corn play a dual role, being ideal forms of carbohydrate and a supplementary source of protein. The best protein sources for strength training are eggs, fish, milk products (the low fat varieties), skinned poultry and lean beef.

The best protein sources are poultry, fish, lean meat and low fat dairy products.

Protein requirements for strength training have been a subject of much controversy over the last decade. Conservative exercise physiologists and nutritionists maintained that athletes require no more protein than non athletes (0.8 to 1 gram of protein per kilogram of bodyweight).

This amount has always been disputed by the bodybuilding and weightlifting fraternity in relation to increased muscle size and strength. Research from eastern bloc countries validates this claim and in recent times there has been an overall revaluation of protein needs for both strength and endurance athletes. Dr D. Telford, head of sports science at the Australian Institute of Sport, in a paper presented to a seminar for elite rowing coaches had the following to say in regard to protein intake:

> In the case of intensive physical activity directed at increasing muscle bulk, the protein requirements of weightlifters have been calculated at 2.2 to 2.6 grams per kilo of bodyweight. This can be obtained without supplementation. In most cases of non muscle hypertrophic training 1.3 to 2.0 grams per kilogram of bodyweight is considered sufficient.

Other researchers have quoted similar figures and it is quite apparent that for strength training where no increase in lean bodyweight is required a figure of 1.5 to 2.0 grams per kilogram of bodyweight would be realistic. If muscle hypertrophy is the aim then 2–2.5 grams per kg would be a reasonable approximation.

In a practical sense, an 80 kg footballer who is pursuing a combined strength and muscle hypertrophy program as part of off season training would be advised to consume around 180–200 grams of protein per day. This would ensure the best results. If the same player was only interested in improving strength/power, 120–160 grams would be sufficient.

The body assimilates protein best if it is consumed in small frequent amounts.

Another relevant factor is that the body assimilates protein best if it is taken in small frequent amounts (somewhere in the region of 25–40 grams per meal). Consequently, for someone engaged in a muscle hypertrophic program five/six smaller balanced meals are preferable to three large meals per day. The use of protein supplements is unnecessary. They are both expensive and of little value over good wholesome food.

Listed below are some of the better protein foods and their value:

One egg	6–8 grams
Chicken flesh (100 grams)	25 grams
Shape or Hi Lo milk (200 ml)	8–10 grams
Skim milk powder (100 grams)	35 grams
Carton of low fat yoghurt	9–11 grams
Cheese/Cotto low fat (100 grams)	25 grams
Grilled fish (100 grams)	20 grams
Lean beef (100 grams)	25 grams

Use low fat dairy products.

Some of these figures are approximate. Most dairy products list protein content (and fat!) on the container. A first class protein drink which is both pleasing to the palate and supplies about 80 grams of protein can be made as follows: Blend together in an electric mixer 500 ml (half a litre carton) of Hi Lo milk, 100 grams of skim milk powder, one egg and either banana and honey or milo and honey. Ensure that the drink is thoroughly blended together. Add the remainder of the carton of milk and chill. Consume throughout the day in three to four servings. This pleasant drink is the ideal difference between a non weight gaining daily food ration and one that is geared towards muscle hypertrophy.

The use of low fat dairy products as a major source of protein serves a variety of purposes. Firstly it assists with adequate calcium intake, and secondly in most instances there is a high water content which contributes towards cleansing the waste products which are a by-product of protein metablism.

Example of a balanced daily meal pattern yielding about 140 grams of protein

Breakfast: One glass of orange juice, two wheatbix and low fat milk, two poached or boiled eggs on toast.

Mid morning: One low fat yoghurt with an apple or banana.

Lunch: Two sandwiches consisting of wholemeal bread, 100 grams of low fat cheese and salad. 200 ml of Hi Lo milk.

Mid afternoon: 200 ml (one large glass) of Hi Lo milk and a piece of fruit.

Evening meal: 250 grams of either fish, skinned chicken or lean beef (grilled) with any two of the following: broccoli, beans, corn, spinach, peas, cabbage. In addition one of the following: potatoes (boiled in jackets/mashed), brown rice or pasta.

Supper: 200 ml of Hi Lo milk or low fat yoghurt or fruit and low fat cheese.

There are a number of alternatives in this meal pattern in order to maintain food satisfaction. For instance tuna can be substituted for one of the meal proteins. The protein content of the daily meal pattern can be lowered by deleting mid morning and mid afternoon snacks. It can be increased by substituting the milk protein drink (as previously described) for plain milk. With a little initiative and imagination there are numerous food combinations that will achieve the desired results.

The body does not store protein.

Finally it should be remembered that the body does not store protein. Once the protein requirements of the body are met, any excess is either used for energy or stored as fat. In addition some is excreted. However it has been estimated that only about 5–10% of total energy requirements in a well nourished individual is supplied from protein in the course of physical exertion. Therefore excessive intake of protein (particularly if it is not a low fat variety) has a reasonable chance of increasing body fat content. Here again genetics (metabolism and body type) play a part.

Fat

Fat is a food element that is essential in small quantities in a balanced diet. However the major problem with most people in affluent western society is overconsumption. Excess dietary fat accumulates under the surface of the skin and hinders athletic performance. As previously mentioned, accumulation of fat around muscle fibre inhibits speed of contraction.

Fat plays a part in the 'energy chain' of human movement, particularly in prolonged continuous exercise in excess of sixty minutes, i.e. long distance running, cycling or swimming. However, even the leanest people have adequate fat storage. So dietary fat should be kept to a minimum. The importance of using low fat dairy products has already been stressed above.

Dietary fat should be kept to a minimum.

With regard to fat consumption, it is very difficult to exclude it totally from the daily diet. Nor is this degree of exclusion desirable. In order to minimise fat intake, butter, margarine and oils should be consumed in small quantities. Many supermarket foods that one would expect to be non fat are actually prepared with fat. Container labels should always be read before purchase. While it is thought that polyunsaturated fats are less harmful than saturated fats, this does not alter the fact that all fats should be kept to a minimum if an athlete is to operate at highest efficiency.

Carbohydrates

Carbohydrates are the body's chief source of energy for strength training.

These are substances that provide the body with its chief source of energy for strength training and the various other physical activities associated with football. They also play a part in the metabolism of protein at a cellular level (the muscle fibre) and some carbohydrates provide fibre, a substance that aids in maintaining a good healthy intestinal system. Carbohydrates also play a part in the body's ability to rid itself of toxic waste.

While a wide variety of foods contain carbohydrates, the most desirable for good health and athletic performance are fruits, vegetables, grains and cereals. These foods are sometimes referred to as 'complex' cabohydrates (the exception is fruit which contains a simple sugar). This group of foods is high in fibre as well as containing quantities of vitamins and minerals.

Fruit, vegetables and grains should occupy a substantial part of the daily food intake.

Fruit, vegetables and grains such as bread, pasta, brown rice and cereals should provide a substantial part of the daily food intake. While complex carbohydrates are important in off season strength training, they are even more vital in both the preseason and competition, when energy demands on the body are considerably greater.

The carbohydrates to be avoided (or at least minimised) are those of a confectionery nature such as cakes, desserts, sugary products, etc., particularly as these also often contain fat. Also, where possible, do not prepare complex carbohydrates in fat or oil. The best modes of cooking are steaming, grilling or microwaving.

As was the case with protein, excess carbohydrates (and to a lesser extent complex carbohydrates) can be stored in the body as fat. However taking into consideration the energy requirements of football players this is unlikely to happen, particularly if mainly complex carbohydrates are consumed.

Fig. 8.1 Whole cereals (minimally refined)—wholemeal breads, brown rice, corn, rye, fibre-rich (bran) cereals, unprocessed bran, muesli, oatmeal

Fig. 8.2 Legumes, nuts, seeds—dried beans, e.g. soy and navy, lentils, chick peas, baked beans

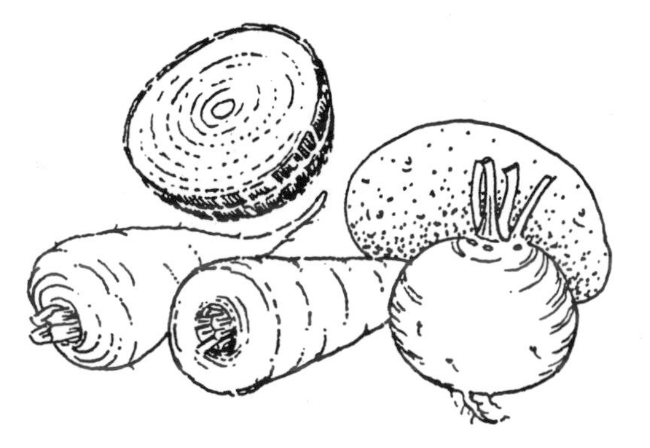

Fig. 8.3 Root vegetables—potatoes, carrots, parsnips, turnips, onions

Fig. 8.4 Fresh and dried fruit, leafy vegetables

Vitamins and minerals

These are substances required in small amounts which perform a number of specific metabolic functions within the body, many of which are important to maximal physical efficiency. As previously mentioned, complex carbohydrates such as fruits, vegetables, grains and cereals contain considerable vitamins and minerals. The same can be said for protein foods of animal origin.

Vitamin and mineral supplementation

This subject has caused considerable controvery in both the field of sport and general health. Most exercise physiologists and nutritionists agree that if a person is eating a balanced diet of ample quantities of fresh food supplementation is not necessary. It has also been generally accepted that vitamin and mineral requirements for athletes are no greater than for the sedentary person. However this traditional viewpoint has recently been challenged by some researchers in the field of exercise nutrition.

There is no doubt that vitamin and mineral deficiencies can impair physical performance.

A number of studies on sportspersons of various disciplines (including football) have revealed deficiencies of various vitamins and minerals. Whether these deficiencies are due to inadequate diet or the rigours of the activity is unclear. One particular study conducted in 1985 on endurance athletes and weightlifters indicated that these sportspersons benefited from multivitamin/mineral supplementation over a twelve months period. This cannot be taken as conclusive evidence as a comparatively small number of test subjects took part. However it does create doubt with regard to the traditional approaches towards vitamin and mineral supplementation.

Another factor to be considered is that some football players have a tendency to indulge in a certain amount of alcohol—on occasions to excess. This in itself can create vitamin deficiencies. Indeed, at a senior level, if there is one aspect of nutrition amongst football players that needs correction, it is in the area of alcohol intake. It would be naive to assume that players would abstain from the traditional 'drink after the game'. However in this age of sporting professionalism where the winning edge keeps becoming smaller, a minimal alcohol consumption is a prerequisite for maximising physical performance (and long term good health!).

Furthermore quite often there is a considerable loss of vitamins and minerals due to modes of cooking and storage factors. This is especially so with the water soluble vitamins, B group and C. Also, while nutritional practices advocated in this chapter would, in most instances, provide adequate vitamins and minerals, some athletes live away from home, sharing a flat etc., eating in restaurants, fast food outlets and other like establishments. Under these conditions it is often difficult to adopt ideal dietary habits.

There is no doubt that vitamin and mineral deficiencies can impair physical performance. Working on the assumption that there may be some doubt as to vitamin and mineral requirements for athletes such as football players, it is in their best nutritional interests to take a reputable multivitamin/mineral capsule either on a daily or alternate day basis. This conclusion is further strengthened by the fact that at times it is difficult for a sportsperson to follow the ideal dietary pattern.

Vitamin and mineral supplementation could be viewed as a form of 'insurance', i.e. if the body does not require it, the amount ingested is non toxic and will be excreted in the urine. Conversely, if there is a need for increased vitamin/mineral intake this contingency is covered. What should be understood is that supplementation is not an easy answer to poor eating habits. It is merely an addition to the nutritional principles outlined.

Reduction of body fat

Up to this point much has been said about nutrition for the football player who is (a) on a strength/power program while maintaining lean muscle mass and (b) on a program of combined increased strength/power and muscle hypertrophy.

However, in Chapter 7 mention was made of the football player who, because of his genetic body type and in certain instances poor nutritional habits, has a marked tendency towards increased body fat in the off season. Indeed this type of player was prescribed an entirely different program for off season training.

Aerobic type activities play an essential part in fat reduction.

A considerable quantity of the program was of an aerobic nature, which apart from maintaining a level of general fitness was geared towards increased rate of body metabolism, something that is essential if this type of individual is to maintain a reasonable level of body fat. What this increased rate of body metabolism means is that aerobic type activities such as running, cycling, swimming, basketball, etc., carried out at a reasonable intensity (pulse rate in the region of 65–80% of maximum) for periods in excess of thirty minutes, increase the rate at which the body 'burns up' food rather than storing it as fat. This process takes place not only when exercising but also when the body is at a lower level of physical activity. In other words there is a 'flow on' of increased metabolic rate from the state of exercise to more sedentary activities.

Fat reduction also requires strict attention to daily food habits.

However, for the type of individual under discussion, a specialised training program is only part of the story. What is of equal importance is attention to daily dietary habits as follows:

1. The diet should emphasise vegetables, grains, fruits, cereals and low fat animal protein foods.

2. Protein consumption should be restricted to 1–1.3 grams per kilogram of bodyweight as this will assist in lowering overall food consumption in terms of calorie intake.

3. Foods such as confectionery, cakes, desserts and any foods prepared in fats and oils should be totally avoided. Alcohol intake should be minimised.

4. Whereas those wishing to gain weight have been advised to eat as much as fix/six times daily, reducers should limit themselves to three daily meals. The diet should be balanced according to the 'healthy diet pyramid' below.

5. The overall quantity of food consumed daily will vary from one individual to another. If the player is strictly adhering to the types of food recommended, together with a suitable training program, and still not achieving a satisfactory result then a reduction of food intake must be implemented. A good idea is to obtain a calorie counter from the local pharmacy and limit food consumption to 1200–1500 calories per day. Once again food intake should be balanced as in the 'healthy diet pyramid'.

Food intake should be balanced as in the 'healthy diet pyramid'.

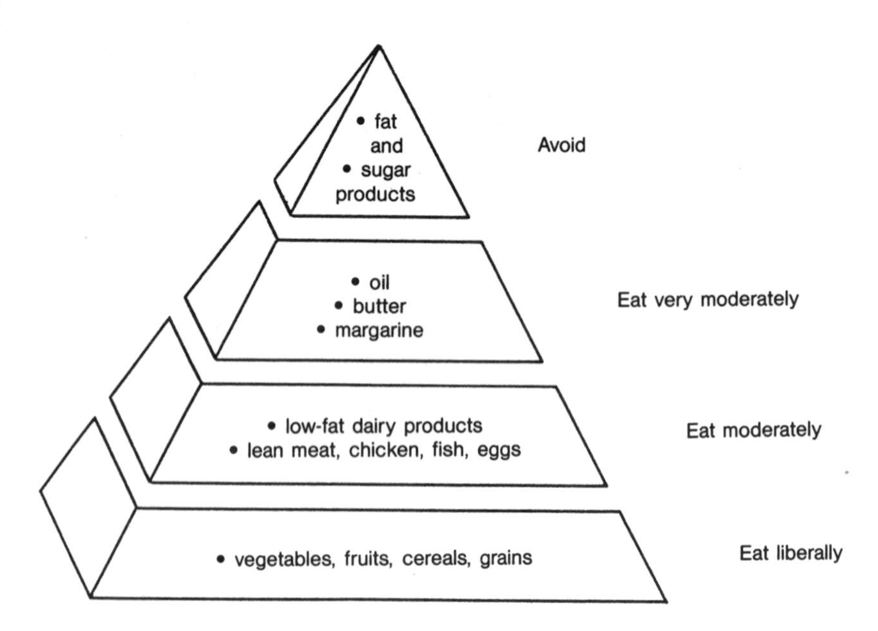

Fig. 8.5 The 'healthy diet pyramid'

The pre game and pre training meal

The pre game meal should be taken three to four hours prior to commencement of play. It should consist predominantly of complex carbohydrates such as pasta, bread or rice with very little fat and moderate protein. The reason for this is that fat and protein take the longest time to digest.

Digestive time for some foods could range from four to six hours.

Digestive time for some foods could range from four to six hours. During the process of digestion of a heavy fat meal, for example the traditional steak and chips, blood is drawn from the muscles and brain to sustain the chore of digestion. Then, when there is a sudden burst of physical activity, an insufficient amount of oxygen carrying blood is available to the muscles and brain where it is now needed. Consequently the body reassigns blood back to the activity sites, short changing the digestive tract. In the biochemical chaos that occurs there is a grave risk of sluggishness, vomiting, fatigue and stomach cramps. It should also be remembered that stress slows digestion and if pre game nerves are intense enough it is not uncommon for a player to unload his stomach contents.

With regard to strength training, it is not always possible to have a three/four hour break from eating. Also the degree of intensity of weight training varies from that of aerobic activities. However there should be a gap of one to one and a half hours from the ingestion of food to commencement of strength training. The most preferable time for training is prior to the evening meal.

Smoking

Whether cigarette smoking is part of nutrition is highly debatable. However as the mouth is the point of entry into the body for this habit, the current chapter is as good a place as any to examine the implications of the practice of smoking.

Smoking impairs physical efficiency.

Smoking is a long term health risk.

Any sportsperson, football player or otherwise, who indulges in cigarette smoking is not only impairing his physical efficiency but is also placing his long term health at great risk. No only has it been established beyond reasonable doubt that smoking is the major cause of lung cancer, but it is a contributor to heart disease. Smoking has also been associated with cancers of the mouth, throat and urinary tract as well as chronic bronchitis and emphysema.

Impairment of physical efficiency occurs in several ways. Firstly the carbon monoxide from smoking combines with a substance in the blood called haemoglobin, which under normal circumstances transports oxygen to all body tissues. This occurs because carbon monoxide has a greater affinity to haemoglobin than oxygen. The inactive compound formed is called carboxyhaemoglobin, which in some smokers inactivates up to 15% of total blood haemoglobin. Therefore the smoking athlete has less haemoglobin available for oxygen transport to vital tissue such as muscle and the heart than would be the case if the same athlete were a non smoker.

However that is not the end of the story. Tarry compounds and other particles collect on the surface of the lungs where air enters, reducing lung efficiency. This type of lung surface damage can cause chronic bronchitis and emphysema, resulting in more rapid and strained breathing in order to inhale sufficient oxygen. In some smokers there is also a reduction in the circulation of blood in the lungs. This further reduces oxygen availability.

Indeed the seriousness of smoking to general health has been reflected in recent government legislature placing severe restrictions on sales promotion of cigarettes.

Summary

Maintaining the dietary habits set out in this chapter is not always convenient. Having to cope with work canteens, eating away from a domestic environment and so on could cause the athlete to either disregard or drastically modify what is recommended. For instance one often hears the platitude 'I haven't time for breakfast'. Getting up fifteen minutes earlier is the simple answer. Failure to do so shows lack of commitment and discipline.

Foresight and determination can overcome most obstacles. Low fat dairy products can be purchased at most supermarkets and transported to the work place on a daily basis. All of the foods recommended in this text are readily available. However, one does not need to become pedantic over nutrition. Commonsense should prevail and the one off situation that occasionally breaks the rules is no cause for alarm. The most important factor is adopting sound nutritional habits on a regular basis.

The Last Word

Man's greatest weakness consists not in failing, but in not rising every time he fails.

In this text the author has endeavoured to give the reader the benefits of 35 years' experience in strength training, both as participant and coach. However it is impossible to cater for every contingency with the written word. If this were not the case there would be no need for individual coaches. All that would be necessary for success in strength training and other physical pursuits would be to read books and journals. Unfortunately life in the fast lane of sport is not so simple. The vagaries of the human body, injuries and other unforeseen factors can combine to upset the best laid plans.

Personal coaching is essential for total development of the athlete. There are times in every athlete's career when academic logic has to be bypassed for a 'flying by the seat of the pants' decision by his coach or mentor. Often the difference between winning and losing can hinge on a 'gut feeling'. This ability to make such a decision is developed through many years of experience in the arena of reality, not the classroom.

What is important and something that the written word can convey is establishing sound principles and guidelines. Therefore readers should endeavour to understand the methodology espoused in this publication and apply it where necessary to the myriad of variables that will occur in strength training in football.

The key to success is the three c's—commonsense, courage and commitment.

Recommended further reading

National Strength and Conditioning Association Journal, PO Box 81410, Lincoln, NE 68508.

John Garhammer, *Sports Illustrated. Strength training*, Harper and Row, Sydney.

Bill Starr, *The Strongest Shall Survive... Strength Training for American Football*, Fitness Products, 129 Severn Avenue, Annapolis, Maryland 2143.

J.C. Radcliffe and R.C. Farentinos, *Plyometrics—Explosive Power Training*, Human Kinetics, Champagne, Illinois.

G. Dintiman, *How to Run Faster*, Leisure Press, New York.

G. Dintiman, R. Ward, *Sport and Speed*, Leisure Press, New York.

Index